Richard III
White Boar

A Novel by Kathleen Ann Milner

Presented by the Healing Arts Series

Chapter Outline

Part II: How This Book Came About

Foreword

In an interview on <u>The D. R. Show</u> on National Public Radio Joe Achenbach stated that his book, <u>The Grand Idea</u>, did not evolve as he originally conceived it. He said that it was like George Washington took over! I was born with psychic abilities and am able to state without reservation that Richard III directed <u>Richard III: White Boar</u>. This book was written and edited in three and a half months. There is no way that I could have done this on my own without the help of personalities who lived the adventure! As quickly as the spirit, who identified himself as Richard III, presented himself, he departed when the tale was told.

You may or may not believe that the spirit of Richard III brought his story to me from the Otherside of the Veil. What you will find is a fascinating story with surprising twists that makes incredible sense. The mystery of who murdered the Princes in the Tower unfolds within the chronological sequencing of events. All of the characters, including Richard, are humanized.

Language patterns and dialects spoken in England in the Middle Ages are like a foreign language to us. Encumbering to read, Old English does not allow the reader to get into the story when so much time is spent translating. So, like <u>Between Two Worlds: The Story of Henry VIII and Anne Boleyn — and Her Celtic Heritage</u>, conversations within this text are written in modern English, though not slang. Slang presents similar problems in a Medieval setting. It takes the reader out of the 15th century surroundings, which the author has spent so much time and effort to recreate. By writing in modern English, readers are better able to get into the story; situations encountered in the 15th century take on modern meaning.

Recipes for dishes mentioned herein are found in The Medieval Cookbook by Maggie Black. It is listed in the *Bibliography* at the end of the book, along with other research books. I was unable to find another text on Richard III that was written in story form complete with dialog except William Shakespeare's play, Richard III.

It is fascinating that while Shakespeare's play is defaming to the extreme, after reading it or watching the production, many people take pity on Richard III, adopting the position that Richard III was framed. Regardless of your position, he is the only dead monarch, who has modern societies, foundations and associations named after him. Was Shakespeare's play merely intended to flatter Queen Elizabeth I? Could Shakespeare have written his play intentionally to make his readers think? Or was it a bit of both? Whenever anyone acts out of character, we wonder why. Shakespeare's Richard III is totally unlike any of his other conflicted, juicy, leading male roles or villains.

As in Between Two Worlds, *Part II* of Richard III: White Boar talks about factors that went into writing this book. Included within *Part II* is the manner in which Richard III's spirit came to me, and how he conveyed the circumstances of his life. I believe that it is the reason why passages herein of Richard III appear to have been written by a man. I also talk about the psychic experiences I encountered in Great Britain that led to unexpected and surprising revelations. Many readers of Between Two Worlds found *Part II* to be as intriguing as *Part I*.

Acknowledgement

Thank you to all of the wonderful people in Great Britain. Many of whom have been mentioned in both this book and in **Between Two Worlds: The Story of Henry VIII and Anne Boleyn — and Her Celtic Heritage.** Thank you to Peter and Brenda Davies, who open their home to me whenever I am in London. A special thank you to Brenda, who has probably trudged through more sites with me than anyone else, and for her valuable insights. Thank you to Marie Scott, for her bravery and resolution of spirit. Thank you to Terry Hedge, who went out of his way to take me to Bosworth Field, and Angela Stevens, who took the day off so that we might visit Middleham Castle.

Thank you to the English Heritage, which does a remarkable job of maintaining the legacy of Britain's historical sites. Jim Anderson and the other erudite guides of the Open Book Visitor Guiding Service provide priceless glimpses into history. Through them, the men and women who lived the adventure take on form.

Thank you to Salie Christopher for introducing me to the Cactus Flower Remedies. Thank you to Jim Wenger for his remarkable work with horses. Thank you to all who have read my previous books and have made this one possible. Thank you God for Your Gifts of the Spirit, Your Grace and the endless possibilities life offers.

The Speaking Stone

Stone of Scone, the ancient speaking stone, found its way to Westminster Abbey as a triumph of the spoils of war. The Stone had once served as Jacob's pillow at Bethal where Jacob was given a visionary dream. He saw his progeny spreading across the earth and ruling as kings up until the time of the Jews return to the Promised Land. When he awoke, Jacob anointed the Stone with holy oil and set it up as an altar in the Great Temple.

In 602 BC, Nabuchadnezzar and the Babylons sacked Jerusalem. Jeremiah and two women of King David's lineage managed to escape with the Stone to Syria. The Stone was later transported from Syria to Egypt and through Sicily and Spain to Ireland, where Saint Patrick blessed it. In Ireland the Stone found another name, *Lia Fail*. When a rightful King of Ireland stepped upon it, the Stone sang. The song was akin to a mountain's bellowing roar, rising from its cavernous bowels up through its deepest crevasses.

When an Irish King lost his holiness, by ordering a man killed in a church, the Stone was brought to Dunaad in Scotland to serve as the coronation throne for the Scottish kings. Restlessly, the Stone move to Iona and then Scone. For more than a thousand years, the Stone of Destiny fulfilled an ancient prophecy:

> Except old seers do feign,
> And wizard wits be blind,
> The Scots in place must reign,
> Where they this stone shall find.

Romans, Vikings and Normans were war-like races fueled by greed and the desire to control. Each in turn had taught the English well. War was a quick means of enriching the vanquisher! The fact that at the end of the day, each conquering nation had been cut adrift in a sea of bankruptcy, losing all seized lands, was a lesson unheeded.

Under the imposing leadership of Edward I, the thirteenth century became England's turn to follow the first lesson of those who had subjected them! The second lesson, the folly of empire building, went ignored! Edward I inherited the good looks and stature, which were characteristic of the Plantagenets. He was strong, skilled in military arts and incredibly lucky, possessing an uncanny savvy for being in the right place at the right time! Edward's goal was to unite the British Isles under the strong leadership of one king — the English King. After years of military campaigning, he managed to bring the Welsh to a state of subjugation. To quell any uprising and protect the western border, Edward built a line of fortified Norman castles in the Welsh Marches or frontier. The predominant fortress was Ludlow Castle.

The English King then began a war against Scotland. His successes in battle earned Edward the name, the Hammer of the Scots. Edward confiscated the Stone of Scone, knowing that the Scots would accept as their leader the king who was crowned on the stone. Upon the Stone's ceremonious arrival in London, in the year of our Lord 1296, Edward had the block of red sandstone placed under the Coronation Throne. The Romans had crushed most of the old ways, but people still believed in the healing power that some stones or gems possessed. Kings understood the power of large stones, especially one such as this!

The Stone had not long resided in its new home when disturbing news was brought to Edward. There was a well-founded rumor that the monks of the Abbey of Scone, where kings of Scotland were traditionally crowned, had hidden the real Stone of Scone. A similar red sandstone block had been substituted to deceive the English. Promptly, Edward discretely dispatched a contingent of soldiers back to Scotland, but the monks had hidden the Stone too well and no amount of coaxing would entice the holy men to reveal their secret. Rather than look the fool, Edward left the pretend stone under the Coronation Throne. He ordered his men to remain silent and he did as well.

It was an innocent enough lie, so Edward thought. He ignored the subtle signs, perhaps, because he did not comprehend them. The scratch under his left rib could have been a bug, but he did not see one. The sourness in the pit of his stomach might well be a piece of undigested meat, but the sensation came and went quickly.

Unbeknownst to Edward, the monks were aware of certain incantations. It began as a prayer to the All Mighty; a petition requesting that the English King would not discover the switch. Then it became something else entirely. While the monks did not consider that what they were doing was black magic, they conjured a curse upon the replacement stone nonetheless.

Royalty dies in the same manner as the commoner. Edward was devastated when his popular queen, Eleanor of Castile, passed away in Nottinghamshire. As a symbol of his grief, he erected crosses in her memory on the journey to Westminster. Edward himself died in Scotland in 1307, weeping on his deathbed, afraid that God would condemn him to hell.

Lack luster so adequately defined and meticulously delineated Edward II's character that he might well have invented the phrase. Above average in height, strapping, flaxen-haired and handsome, Edward's outward appearance proved to be an empty husk. Ambitionless with regards to military conquest, he also had little interest in matters of state! His major aspiration and preoccupation as king was the enrichment of himself and his friends. He avoided at all costs any sport associated with kings, preferring instead menial, energy-efficient tasks and hobbies.

It was not Edward's fault that he inherited a treasury, exhausted from years of war and a populace, discontented with the resulting burdens of high taxes. Edward, however, added to his difficulties by frequently antagonizing feudal magnates. After losing the Battle of Bannockburn to the Scottish, who fought under the leadership of Robert Bruce, the Scots ravaged northern England unopposed. Rather than engage the Scots in combat, the governing body of lords, led by Thomas of Lancaster, fought against the King's party. Only through the efforts of the noble Earl of Pembroke were the two feuding factions reconciled.

The dysfunctional kingdom would have been put straight were it not for Edward II's insistence on absolute rule. An additional rub to the lords was that he depended on the advise of only two men, whom he showed with riches. Edward had not learned his lesson! He had not changed his ways!

All in all, Edward II was nobody's idea of a proper medieval king. His queen, Isabella, detested Edward most of all - so much so, that she and her lover, Roger Mortimer of Wigmore, arranged to have the King detained and murdered. Hoping to make it look as if Edward had died of natural causes, a hot poker was rammed up into his bowels. While the deed was carried out surreptitiously in Berkeley Castle, suspicions and rumors circulated throughout the realm. An English bard christened Isabella the she-wolf of France. Undaunted, Isabella piously attended her late husband's funeral. Afterwards, she happily assumed her new role as Queen Dowager of England.

As a couple, Edward and Isabella were incongruously mismatched. As king, Edward was unpopular among lords and commons alike. Who could have predicted that from Edward II's loins would arise a king by whom all future English kings would be measured?

Edward Plantagenet was crowned Edward III in 1327. Chivalrous and affable, Edward III resembled his father in appearance alone! The new King Edward was tolerant, and he proved to have superb generalship skills and dynamic leadership qualities. He knew how to throw a good medieval party! He brought culture to his court, including the poetry of Dante, who had died in 1321.

In 1328, the French king died without an heir. Through his mother, Edward III laid claim to the French throne. However, France did not recognize inheritance through women. Charles' cousin, Philippe de Valois, was named king.

Mortimer had been created Earl of March and he used Ludlow Castle as his base. Biding his time, Edward III waited for Mortimer to overstep his bounds. In 1330, Edward at last had Mortimer seized and executed. Mortimer's lover, Edward III's mother, Queen Isabella, was confined in Castle Rising in Norfolk.

After defeating Robert Bruce and his Scottish followers, and thereby securing the northern boarder, Edward III turned his attention back to France. In 1338, Edward III initiated the Hundred Years War against the French. The English expected military successes from their kings and the booty wars brought home. Edward looked toward France with a general's eye. Military achievement would regain lost French territory, increase England's political foothold on Continental Europe and secure trading privileges for English merchants. Needless to say, military glory would strengthen Edward's position.

English soldiers were paid to fight. In addition, military victories afforded Medieval armies the opportunity to loot, rape and burn. Soldiers considered it their right to seize the spoils of war. Surgeons traveled with the militia; their major duty was the amputation of mangled or gangrenes limbs. Oftentimes, men died from the shock of surgery, which were performed without anesthesia. Men bled to death due to primitive conditions.

War was brutal hand to hand combat where men were butchered on the field! The English longbow altered the dynamics of war, as it proved to be a superior weapon. Firing their arrows in unison, bowmen sent a prodigious wave of arrows through the air, killing many of the enemy with each volley. After softening the opponent, knights hacked with axes, slashed with swords and speared their opponents. At the end of each day of battle, bodies were piled high and the air itself, hung heavy, as if with the souls of the dead. The stench of death left a thick coating in the mouths and on the teeth of the living. The unmistakable reek permeated soldiers' hair and somehow managed to cling to the very shirts and undergarments worn under their armor.

Edward triumphed in France and his English subjects loved him. To ennoble war and the virtues of chivalry, Edward III instituted the Most Noble Order of the Garter in 1348. The brotherhood consisted of twenty-six English knights sworn to uphold moral values of heroism, conduct and honor expounded by King Arthur and Saint George. Knightly virtues of integrity, generosity, compassion, comradery and loyalty were espoused. Knights were expected to courageously and skillfully defend the oppressed, demonstrate gallantry towards women, and all the while possess a gay, frank spirit and exhibit personal growth. Edward even had a large round table built in Windsor Palace.

From 1347 to 1349, the Black Death swept through Europe, killing a third of the population. For over two years, two hundred people died daily in London. Families and friends of the diseased paid the Church for indulgences. People threw their garbage and waste into the streets and wondered why God had sent the bubonic plague upon them.

Christ's Vicar in Rome provided the answer for the scourge beset upon humanity; he proclaimed that it was a spell invoked by witches and Jews. Pope Gregory IX founded the Inquisition in 1231, and subsequent popes continued to use it as a handy tool to squelch blasphemy should anyone dare to question Church doctrines. If the pope said the world was flat that was that! The Inquisition was also a 'money maker'. After all, someone had to pay for a witch's arrest, imprisonment, torture and execution. Why not the witch and her family? When John XXII died in 1334, he was the wealthiest man in the whole world.

During Edward's reign, the appearance of the Little Ice Age and the virulent Black Plague caused millions of deaths throughout Europe. These catastrophes also proved to be the harbinger of change. In the near future, these events would impact the entire economic and social structure of Western Europe. Out of great tragedy would rise opportunity!

An ice age had begun in 1303, freezing the Baltic Sea. The sudden, colder climate resulted in a shortened growing season. Consequently, harvests were smaller, which brought about hunger and starvation for countless serfs.

In 1361, despite prayers, penances and offerings, the Black Death returned. Children accounted for most of the fatalities because of their weaker immune systems. Symptoms started with boils under the armpits and the groin. As if living flesh were rotting in a stench beyond

7

description, purplish-black blotches appeared all over the body. Blood and puss leached from the boils. Soon the victim was spitting blood. Doctors checked their patients' urine for blood. If blood was found, hope was lost. People usually died in three days after contacting the disease. English doctors offered a number of cures ranging from freshening the air by throwing herbs into the fireplace, or letting blood out of the body by opening a vein or using leaches. They also sold crushed pearls and emeralds to the wealthy for consumption.

Fewer serfs, meant fewer men in the work force; a day's work was becoming a valuable commodity. Men were able to leave the land so they might sell their labor or become merchants. Serfdom was slowly ending! Those in power often see origins of change as threats to their authority. Thus, the affluent tenaciously attempted to hold on to the system of slavery. Only a scant few of the nobility had the foresight to see the inevitability of change and the potential opportunities it afforded. After all, the prosperous middle class in Venice enriched the upper class.

Wool was England's chief export. It was a valuable commodity that was used for cloth and clothing. Wool tapestries hung on walls to keep the cold out in the winter. Wool trade provided a means of revenue for both secular merchants and the monasteries. Merchants from as far away as the Baltic and Mediterranean sailed to English ports. Wool provided a stable income for the merchants and those who raised sheep, as well as dyers, weavers, designers and embroiderers. Directly or indirectly many fashioned their income from the trade. In 1353, Edward III made an agreement with the merchants allowing them to control the wool trade. Soon, the Merchants of the Staple became a powerful, influential and wealthy body.

Edward III was productive and prolific in his personal life as well. He had ten legitimate children — Edward, The Black Prince, who died before his father; Isabella; Joan; Lionel of Antwep, Duke of Clarence; John of Gaunt, Duke of Lancaster; Edmund of Langley, Duke of York; Mary; Margaret; and Thomas of Woodstock, Duke of Gloucester. Most of Edward's children were married to sons and daughters of the great houses of his realm. This further secured his popularity as well as the throne.

In addition to the many legitimate royals, John of Gaunt had a long affair with Catherine Swynford. The English in the Middle Ages were forgiving of men, especially young bachelors, for their indiscretions. The chivalrous action, however, was to recognize and support bastard children. John of Gaunt did both! Catherine's illegitimate children were named the Beauforts, after the French castle where they were raised. They were later legitimized but they were not granted the rights of inheritance. The English felt it was unlucky for a bastard or his progeny to reign! A passage from the Bible supported this belief.

The year 1360 was the pinnacle of Edward III's reign. The following year, the Black Plague returned with a vengeance. At the same time, the French cause was gaining momentum.

English occupation was exceedingly unpopular in France! In 1364, Charles IV ascended to the French throne and led a rebellion against the English. By 1369, the French successfully plundered and burned Portsmouth. It was also the year Edward's Queen of forty years, the well-loved Philippa, died. Edward, left with a crumbling dynasty, longed for former days of glory.

Edward took a mistress, Alice Perrers, who bore him three illegitimate children. In 1377, Alice watched Edward take his last breath at Sheen Palace after a stroke confined him to his bedchamber. The body was still warm when Alice stole the King's rings and disappeared.

The year before Edward's death, his eldest son, the Black Prince, died, but not before turning against his father's politics. It left Edward a weakened man. England was vulnerable as well - the English treasury was depleted! Edward died, leaving his entire kingdom gasping for breath from high taxes, necessary to support and maintain a military presence in France. The French were indignantly occupied. They, too, were infuriated over high English taxes. Without Edward III's leadership and the funds necessary to maintain occupation, the French were taking back their country, piece-by-piece, town-by-town.

Richard II was ten-years old when he inherited his grandfather's throne. He was the son of the Black Prince, who had been renowned for his valor and distinguished by his violent temper. The unpopular John of Gaunt became England's Steward and Richard's prop to the throne. However, there were problems with other English barons, who resented the power of the Protector. It was not that the barons lacked entitlement! By the political power of patronage the lords had become an immensely privileged class that had developed expensive preferences. After four decades of arraying men to arms, each baron had his own private army.

Richard, while brave, proved to be particularly unhandy at generalship and the skills of war. When French military campaigns ended, discharged soldiers roamed the land as highwaymen. This did nothing to bolster Richard's popularity!

What Richard was particularly good at was establishing a magnificent court. His fabulous garments, elaborate cuisines and brilliant entertainment raised the bar for luxury. His glittering court was alive with minstrels and music. Ladies were in attendance! Their presence inspired the evolvement of courtly social behavior into the decadent game of chivalrous love, whereby courtesans and ladies-in-waiting played out roles similar to those found in romantic fiction. Knighthood also became a courtly pursuit, as opposed to the ferocity of hands-on, in-the-field combat. Most eccentric of all the characters in Richard II's Medieval court drama was the King himself. He had Sheen Palace demolished after his wife, Queen Anne, died in it.

At the other extreme of the social ladder, peasants were becoming discontent. In 1381, the Peasant's Revolt broke out. Serfs marched to the tune, "When Adam delved and Eve span, who was then the gentleman?" Rebellion ended with the death of Wat Tayler. When order was restored, Richard reneged on his promises of reform.

Towards the end of his reign, Richard insisted on ruling as an absolute despot. He could do without the help of Parliament, thank you! This along with his incessant greed created insecurity amongst the lords, which left open the door for another to become king.

A king's base of power necessitated the support of his subjects, particularly, the greater subjects. This class consisted of lords and gentry, who held local government offices as constables, sheriffs and stewards, who benefited from their social positions. A dozen or so dukes and earls at the very top of the social ladder were considered magnates. They each held their own courts, which were fashioned after the king's. Magnates enjoyed both political power and autonomy!

Many of the magnates were related to Edward III and possessed vast estates and enormous wealth. Magnates each had a retinue of servants, who by a feudal system of indenture of retainer waited on their masters' peacetime and military requirements. On the one hand, magnates were able to accumulate titles and wealth through marriage; on the other, magnates lost holdings if they found themselves on the wrong side of a political cue. In such cases, the crown confiscated their titles and assets, which were either held or doled out to reward faithful courtiers. The future of a spouse of such a disentitled magnate was entirely dependent upon the lord who took her and her young children in.

Henry Bolingbroke, the Earl of Derby, the only surviving son of John of Gaunt and his first wife, Blanche of Lancaster, managed to usurp the throne from his cousin, the rightful king, Richard II, in 1399. Thus, the handsome, short, red-haired new King, Henry IV, established the House of Lancaster as rulers of England. Richard II had no children to challenge Henry's claim; however, the Earls of Huntington, Kent and Salisbury led a rebellion against the newly crowned King. The insurrection was put down, but Henry knew that the old King would always be a threat to his rule. Henry ordered Richard smothered in his prison cell at Pontefract Castle. Rumors were circulated that Richard had starved himself to death, at roughly the same time that the celebrated author, Geoffrey Chaucer, died.

Meanwhile, on the Continent, King Charles IV of France refused to recognize Henry IV as king because Charles' daughter, Isabella, had been married to Richard II. Politically, situations worsened when Henry sent the Dowager Queen packing back to France without her jewelry. Charles IV responded by aiding Welsh rebels. However, Charles suffered from bouts of insanity that reduced him to a virtual state of paralysis without memory, speech or reason. He came to believe that he was made of glass. To prevent himself from smashing to smithereens, he had iron rods sewn into his clothes in case he fell down. Unsurprisingly, Charles' efforts against the English King were badly planned, uncoordinated and insufficiently funded.

Throughout his reign, by whit and luck Henry IV maintained his hold on the crown of England from an onslaught of rebellious barons — real and imagined. Fear beleaguered his mind that another claimant to the crown would do unto him what he had done unto to Richard. In addition, deep pangs of guilt and remorse beset him. He suffered from ill health. His turmoil was exacerbated by a lice infestation from hell. Nothing could induce the little buggers to leave. Vermifuge was ineffectual! At forty-seven years old, he died an old man before his time in 1413. He had sat on the throne for thirteen years of problematic rule.

In his will Henry IV had requested that he be buried at Canterbury. Since roads were filled with potholes, Henry's remains were escorted by boat down the Thames River. When a severe storm cropped up, the crew thought the ill-fated, old king's bad luck would sink their boat. So, the sailors threw the body overboard! After the tempest subsided, they substituted another body before reaching their final destination.

Henry V was a rare man who shaped history to his own design. His first concern as King was to restore those who had suffered under his father's reign - the supporters and relatives of Richard II. Furthermore, Richard's body was exhumed and reburied with ample pomp and pageantry at Westminster. Now freed from the paralysis of internal conflicts, the new King Henry turned his attention to French conquest.

While Charles IV was going mad, the Duke of Burgundy took the opportunity to have the Duke of Orleans assassinated. Henry V responded to the murder by aligning himself with the Burgundies faction. This resulted in a lengthy but successful military campaign against the French, the most decisive victory for the English being at Agincourt.

Many French prisoners were taken at the battle of Agincourt. Henry ordered them held in back of the English line. When the French attacked again, concerned that the prisoners might get free and attack him from the rear, Henry V ordered all of the bound prisoners killed. Henry's reasoning did not stop the French from holding the English King most accountable for the bloody, unmerciful slaughter.

As part of the treaty settlement with the defeated Charles IV, Henry became Regent of France and married Charles' daughter, Catherine. Henry loved her dearly. Henry had spent most of his reign in France, much to the dismay of the English Parliament, but he returned to England for Catherine's coronation. The couple then went on a royal progress that took them as far west as the Welsh Marches and north to the city of York. During this time, Catherine conceived, giving birth to a son. Afterwards, Henry returned to France and the fighting that was necessary to maintain English occupation.

Henry V reigned for only nine years. He died from dysentery on French soil in August 1422. At the time of his death, England and her Burgundiase allies held French provinces north of the Loire, as well as Guienne. During his reign, Henry V brought wealth to his subjects at the enormous expense of war. As a bitter reminder that people everywhere resist occupation, French patriots at Loire assassinated Henry's brother, Clarence, shortly before Henry V died.

Love Without Power

Henry VI ascended to the English throne at the ripe old age of 9 months. Six weeks later with the death of his grandfather, Charles VI, Henry VI was declared King of France. While Henry V would have had the single-mindedness of purpose to benefit from the happenstance, the infant King's regents did not. The nineteen-year-old son of Charles VI was named Charles VII and as the Dauphin, he ruled southern France. Northern France was governed in the English King's name by John, Duke of Bedford. Neither man had the resolution of spirit, nor the military or diplomatic skill to unite France one-way or the other.

The baby King's inheritance included a meager treasury, grossly depleted by crushing costs of war. Yet, more funds were required for retaining high-maintenance English troops encamped in a foreign land. Commons balked over the high taxes necessary to support the troops and continue the French occupation.

Henry V in his will had nominated his brother, Humphrey, Duke of Gloucester, as Regent of England. The peers, however, insisted that Humphrey govern as Protector with the consent of the Council. Thus, during the long minority reign, an embittered battle ensued for control between Humphrey and Henry Beaufort, Bishop of Winchester and Cardinal. The conflict left in its wake feuding magnates, a bankrupt court and English commercial trade brought to its knees.

In 1428, Henry was placed under the guardianship of Richard Beauchamp, Earl of Warwick. Henry's mother, Dowager Queen Catherine, was not included in the upbringing of her son or any other matter of importance. She lived a secluded life apart from court, quietly forgotten. In her loneliness, a handsome, dashing, Welsh clerk from an Anglesey family of modest background, Owen Tudor, became her lover.

The valiant Henry V had been the cement holding the empire together. After his death, the French territories began eroding away. The Maid's trumpets of war in 1429, and the crowning of the Dauphin as Charles VII at Rheims signaled this fact to the world.

Two years later, ten-year-old Henry VI witnessed the burning of Joan of Arch at Rouen, but the damage had been done. To the humiliation of the English, restoration of the Valois rule was seemingly inevitable. Currently, England maintained a tenuous hold on Guienne, Maine and Normandy. Insurgents, starving French peasants, cut the throats of the hated English whenever the opportunity presented itself. Bands of mercenaries played for both or either side, or ravaged the French countryside on their own behalf.

On December 2, 1431, nineteen-year old Richard Plantagenet was among those who witnessed the meaningless coronation of Henry VI as King of France at Saint Denis in Paris. Henry VI was the first and only English king to be crowned king of France. While the English celebrated the coronation, others, like Duke Phillip of Burgundy, read the inimitable handwriting on the wall. In 1435, Phillip of Burgundy deserted the English all together by making a separate treaty with Charles VII. Henry VI burst into tears when his spies brought him the news.

At this time, William de la Pole, Earl of Suffolk, headed Cardinal Beaufort's party. Humphrey, Duke of Gloucester, was in disgrace — his wife, Eleanor, had been condemned as a witch. However, Humphrey found a supporter in Richard Plantagenet, Duke of York.

Richard Plantagenet, Duke of York, traced his peerage to Edmund of Langley, Duke of York, on his father's side and Lionel of Antwerp, Duke of Clarence, on his mother's side. When the last male Mortimer died without an heir in 1425, Ludlow Castle passed on to the son of Anne Mortimer, Richard Plantagenet. By his lineage and his wealth, Richard Plantagenet was the greatest lord in the realm.

Richard of York was naturally charming and possessed an easy, jovial nature. He was close to average height, dark-haired and had a muscular, square frame. Though not fashionably blond, tall, or handsome, as was the hallmark of the Plantagenet's, Richard was good looking in his own way. To boot, he was personable, fair in his dealings with others regardless of their rank, and he possessed boundless energy. Unlike many men of his time, Richard's heart was not hardened by unquenchable ambition and insatiable greed; he was an honest man who respected justice.

In 1437, eighteen-year old Henry VI sat on the illustrious Coronation Throne. Piously, he wore a hair shirt and frequently prayed. Generously, he established foundations at Eton and King's College. Pacifistically, he often interceded to spare the lives of the condemned. Priggishly, he avoided any sexual overtures as well as scantly dressed women. Contemplatively, he avoided secular affairs, leaving the management of the kingdom and treasury to others. Not a slave to fashion, Henry wore a farmer's rounded-toed, heavy shoes and a townsman's long, black, hooded gown. Over his tall but fragile frame he wore a full-length coat. Like his father and his grandfather, Henry traced his ancestry back to not only Edward III, but Edward II as well.

Henry VI's mother, the Dowager Queen Catherine, died during the same year. It was then that her affair with Owen Tudor was disclosed and the fact that they had three illegitimate children together — Jasper, Edmund and Owen. The King's Council was livid! They felt that Catherine had slighted the memory of Henry V through her illicit relationship. Owen Tudor claimed that he and Catherine had been married, but he was unable to produce any evidence or witnesses whatsoever. Catherine's lover was cast into Newgate prison. However, the wily Owen managed to escape!

The aftermath of the Dowager Queen's affair seemed of little importance to Richard Plantagenet, Duke of York. In 1438, Richard wed Cecily Neville, the beautiful Rose of Raby and daughter of Ralph Neville, Earl of Westmorland. Cecily was seven years older than Richard, but it didn't matter; he was thunderstruck the first time he saw her.

In the early 1440's Richard served as the King's Lieutenant in France; Cecily joined her husband after his arrival on the Continent. Richard governed the English holdings firmly, though he had insufficient troops and meager funding. Three of the couple's children were born at Rouen. Edward was born in April 1442; Edmund was born the following year. Elizabeth arrived soon after.

In 1444, Henry VI's favorite, the Earl of Suffolk, arranged for him to wed Charles VII's niece, Margaret of Anjou. Dazzlingly beautiful, fiery and arrogant, the fifteen-year old Margaret was the antithesis of the twenty-four-year old, monk-like Henry. What the Earl did not tell Henry was that he had heard it whispered that the Anjou family practiced black magic. How ridiculous, members of a royal family practicing witchcraft! Hardly worthwhile mentioning to Henry!

Upon Margaret's arrival in England, she quickly discovered that, like Henry's advisors, she was able to mold her husband's will to her own. She persuaded Henry to secretly relinquish the county of Maine to Charles VII. By the time the news leaked out, Maine was firmly in French control. Englishmen were infuriated by the royal betrayal. Fearing a mob scene, Parliament was forced to meet at Bury to avoid incensed Londoners. Suffolk persuaded the new Queen that her unpopularity was due to York and Gloucester; certainly, not due to any of her actions. As Gloucester and York were in favor of bringing lost French territory back under English control, Margaret was easily convinced. Suffolk took further advantage of the situation by talking Henry into having the Duke of Gloucester arrested on the treasonous grounds that he was planning a rebellion. Within five days after his apprehension, the Duke died while in custody. Rumors persisted that Suffolk had ordered Gloucester's demise.

Undeterred by ingenuous gossip, Suffolk was determined to advance himself further through military accomplishment. With the consent, blessing and backing of the King, Suffolk led a military campaign against the Duke of Brittany, Charles VII's ally. Charles countered by invading Normandy, forcing Suffolk to surrender; thus, bringing the Duchy of Normandy back under French control. By November, Somerset was impelled to surrender Rouen and surrounding towns in exchange for a secure, safe passage back to England for his family and himself.

Humiliated, the British were out for blood! King Henry failed utterly in his attempt to save Suffolk, who was caught shortly after his return to England and assassinated by an angry mob! This event followed the murder of the Bishop of Salisbury. England was in defiance!

Not long after Suffolk's demise, Jack Cade, the leader of a rebellious Kentish army, forced the King and Queen to flee from London to Kenilworth. What disturbed Londoners the most was

19

that their pleadings to the royal couple not to abandon them were ignored. What most disconcerted the King and Queen was that after they left London, nobody cared enough to stop Jack Cade.

John Beaufort, Duke of Somerset was nearly as unpopular and corrupt as Suffolk. Furthermore, Somerset was associated with Suffolk's French debacle. Regardless, Somerset became the King's and Queen's new favorite. As if that wasn't enough to cause disruption, Somerset was the sworn enemy of the powerful Richard, Duke of York! By 1445, Somerset had enough influence to block the renewal of York's appointment as the King's Lieutenant in France. Somerset and the Queen had the King's ear!

Gossip persisted concerning the Queen and Somerset. Margaret's popularity plummeted, but not all rumors about the Queen were true; dogs did not bark at her when she halted or passed by. The favored Lancastrians loved her, and she had her good points! In 1448, she founded Queen's College in Cambridge. In a gesture of gratitude, one of the false hammerbeams was carved in the shape of an angel, which bore a crowned shield embossed with the letter "M" for Margaret.

To gain a greater control over the House of Lords, in 1449, Somerset urged Henry to appoint the Duke of York the Lieutenant of Ireland. Thus, York was successfully removed from court. Somerset was not entirely satisfied; a more devious plot spun in his ambitious mind. Before setting out for Ireland, the Duke was warned that Somerset had set traps along the route to the sea. York managed to evade them all, including a force led by Thomas Stanley. In Ireland York governed with fairness by establishing justice and maintaining order. He made friends with the chieftains and won the hearts of the Irish. His son, George, was born in Dublin.

In 1450, Cade's rebellion offered the Duke of York an excuse to return unsummoned to England, where outpouring of raging discontent brewed ubiquitously. The realm reeled from stupefying mismanagement and unbridled corruption. Avaricious advisors and dishonest officers of the household had done their worst. By pillaging the crown's lands, rifling the treasury and embezzling household funds, they left Henry VI owing £400,000 and only a meager yearly income that did not cover expenses. To reach King Henry at Westminster, Richard again had to avoid Somerset's traps. York's superior forces easily arrived in London.

Henry VI was dwarfed in the presence of the Duke of York. Anxiously, the King feared that his cousin, Richard, had come to claim his crown. After all, Henry's Queen frequently reminded him that the Duke of York's hereditary claim to the throne of England was stronger than his own. Richard of York's three uncles had all died childless and after six years of marriage, Margaret had failed to conceive. York and his son, Edward, were next in line to the crown.

The Duke of York had not come to oust Henry VI. Richard Plantagenet was content with his station in life and all that entailed. He understood well that upholding the honor and dignity of the King's position ensured his hereditary rank and holdings, as well as the status of the other lords. If the commons were to question the King's hereditary authority, he and the other lords would be next. York's sole purpose was to have Henry renounce Somerset and to assume his own rightful position in the Council. Furious, the Duke eyed his sniveling cousin. Pausing, Richard reassured Henry, "I am your lord's true liegeman, why do you send men to intercept me, to do me harm on my journeys?"

Henry barely breathed. He struggled for an acceptable answer. At last he blurted out, "I was advised that your motives were unworthy." Henry paused, "But I now see otherwise." Henry hesitated again, "And I now declare you my true subject and faithful cousin."

The Duke had long mulled over which words he would impress upon the King when they met. "As you have acknowledged me, I demand my rightful place in the Council. Your closest advisors have bankrupted the treasury, England is near anarchy and the government must be restored. You are the King! The people look to you to take control and reinstate order!"

Henry stammered, "I am a lover of good government! I am a good and pious King!"

"Then take the first step, cousin! Summon Parliament!"

England was but one of many nation-states that were emerging from feudal societies. The English king, who exercised his authority through the Office of the Exchequer, Office of the Chancery and the courts, headed the government from Westminster Palace. The king was independent from Parliament, in that he maintained his household and costs of the court by deriving an income from royal estates. He also had the authority to call or dismiss Parliament at will.

Parliament consisted of two houses: By hereditary right, the heads of some fifty noble families along with leading clerics sat in the House of Lords. The gentry controlled the House of Commons. While Parliament did not share a role in government, it was only through Parliament that the king was able to raise taxes or subsidies.

Henry VI called Parliament together in October. Backing the Duke of York, both the Lords and Commons demanded reforms! Somerset was arrested on crimes of misgovernment. The Duke of York was acknowledged as the first councilor of the King.

By December, rage replaced Queen Margaret's fear. Gathering up herself as well as her forces, she easily bent the King back to her will. Somerset was released from prison and granted the positions of Comptroller of the royal Household and Captain of Calais. The fox was truly in the henhouse! By the spring, the King dissolved Parliament, shortly after convening. The Speaker of the Commons was imprisoned for audaciously proposing that the Duke of York be formally recognized as heir to the throne. Revolted by Henry's sheer lack of control, York returned to Ludlow Castle in the Welsh Marches.

Henry and Margaret were still childless, but the King refused to name his heir! York was clearly next in line; Somerset was Henry's friend. However, the ever-striving Somerset only had a weak claim to the throne through the Beaufort line of John of Gaunt. Somerset resorted to set about turning the King once again against York. Along with Queen Margaret, they persistently told contrived tales of York's conspiracy and aspiration. Fearing an uprising if he named Somerset heir apparent, Henry declined to name Somerset. In extreme matters, Henry did have a moderating influence on the Court, but Margaret and Somerset were doggedly determined! In January 1452, word was brought to Richard of the King's hostility towards him. When Henry failed to respond to his messenger, York assembled an army and marched on London. He found the city's gates closed and the King and his forces camping at Blackheath. This time, it was Queen Margaret, who had amassed a superior force. However, the Duke had friends amongst the nobles in the royal camp. They sent a contingent to determine the Duke's demands. York's terms had not altered. The Duke responded, "Somerset must be brought to trial and I want my rightful place on the Council!"

Henry's captains persuaded the King to concede to York's demands and swear to it upon the royal oath. When news was brought back to the Duke, York quietly disbanded his army. Afterwards, he approached Henry's tent with only a few men. He was taken aback in shock and abhorrence to discover Somerset and the Queen in control. The King's word meant nothing! York was promptly arrested, but his enemies quickly came to realize and fear that the popular Duke's execution might well insight the populace. Revolt would result in their demise!

It was when the Queen and Somerset heard that Richard's ten-year-old son, Edward, was marching towards London at the head of a immense force that they were forced to release the Duke. Before he was set free, York was made to swear an oath. At Saint Paul's, before Lords and Commons alike, Richard swore his allegiance to Henry VI. He promised obedience, swearing never to raise arms against the King. Humbled, York returned to his keep at Fotheringhay Castle and to Cecily, who was in her eleventh pregnancy.

The story had not ended; it was only beginning. Red and white roses were the hallmarks of the feuding lords - red belonging to the Beaufort line of John of Gaunt and white symbolizing the influential House of York. Somerset's envy of the Duke of York had turned to loathing. On the other hand, York was anxious to secure his rightful place in the Council and to bring good government and justice to England. A principled man, he detested the injustice and corruption that spawned from Somerset's mismanagement and manipulation of the King. From the bottomless, irreparable rift between Somerset and York, and the biased meddling of Queen Margaret in the affairs of state, the War of the Roses evolved.

Jolly Old Duke of York

Jolly old Duke of York,
He had ten thousand men.
Marched them all up the hill,
And then back down again.
When he was up he was up,
When he was down he was down.
When he was only half way up,
He was neither up nor down.

Nearly three quarters of England lay wooded, providing habitat for a diversity of creatures. Elk, deer, bears, badgers, wolves, boars and others roamed the great forests freely, striving to maintain a balance amongst one another and man. Nature, flush with abundance, was looked upon solely as a commodity — fresh game and sport for the wealthy, potential farmland for the peasants. With the old ways long forgotten, English history definitively began with the Roman conquest.

Everywhere Rome conquered soldiers drove asunder any idea that God's Spirit was to be found in nature. Only in Ireland had the Romans invaded but not conquered. In Eire, influential Romans traveled to study alchemy, learning to call forth the elements and use the power inherent in the earth. However, the Celts were not about ready to reveal all they knew to a warmongering society.

Romans were the inventors of cement. With it they built impressive aqueducts and roads – although, much of their engineering left with them in 410. Roman structures disappeared as men used the stones for new buildings and pasture fences. Superstition became a pale replacement for the wisdom of the Celts. In Rome, Christ's Vicars twisted Christ's teachings into the Holy Inquisition. Only now and again was a soul born into body, bringing with him or her some remembrance of the old ways.

Fotheringhay Castle was the Duke of York's favorite castle. It had been built by Simon de Senlis in the 12th century on the north bank of the River Nine and was in Scottish control until 1294. In 1377, Edward III gave Fotheringhay manor and castle to his son, Edmund of Langley, the first Duke of York and founder of the powerful House of York. Edmund replaced wooden buildings with a stone structure and re-edified the entire castle.

Fotheringhay now loomed high above the tree line as an imposing Norman defensible fortress. Double stone motes further protected the castle on the remaining sides. Masses of stone battlements and towers rose up to form an octagonal keep, the heart of the castle. The Duke's soldiers guarded the large ditched outer bailey, or defensive wall surrounding the outer court of the castle, at the gatehouse.

After crossing the drawbridge and leaving the gatehouse, visitors, dignitaries, guests and petitioners were confronted with the formidable inner bailey wall and a second mote. The second drawbridge ended at the Captain's Tower, which served as the gatehouse to the inner bailey. Narrow, round-headed windows in the Captain's Tower provided lighting for the first floor, which contained the winding gear that lowered and raised the massive portcullis, which were made of thick, heavy iron grating. The Captain's Tower projected forward so that soldiers were able to protect either side of the wall. In addition to the portcullis, three sets of enormous double doors protected the entrance passage. Murder holes in the ceiling of the passageway allowed the defenders to hurl objects (hot nails) or liquid (hot water or waste from the privy) onto the would-be assailants, making armor extremely uncomfortable. Oil was entirely too precious a commodity to heat and use for defensive purposes!

The inner bailey was decorated with Gothic tracery. The stables were immediately to the left so that the horses could be led easily across the drawbridges to the grassy unfortified half of the island to graze. There were quarters for the officers and a barracks for the soldiers, a kitchen that prepared food for those who served in the castle and a church. Privies were located throughout the castle and consisted of a hole that emptied into the mote.

The keep was freestanding with massively thick walls. The only entry being a flight of stairs to the first floor, making it more difficult for enemy forces to gain the leverage and speed to ram down the door. A spine wall ran the full height of the keep, dividing it into two equal halves, each independently defensible. Internal staircases ran at opposite sides of the building. Storage facilities and the kitchen were located on the ground floor. The great timbered hall was on the first floor, as were the private apartments of the Duke and Duchess, who had their own private chapel. On the second floor, the cooks prepared meals for the family and their guests in a small Norman kitchen. Most of the food preparation was done on tables in the middle of the kitchen and the cooking in the fireplace, with the chimney rising through the thickness of the wall. Projecting stones inside the chimney allowed the chimney sweeps access.

Breakfast for the wealthy included four meat courses. Twelve courses of meat and fish were served at noon, while the evening meal consisted of pies and meat. Ale was safer to drink than the water.

Respiratory and digestive problems were a frequent complaint, so, people often slept propped up in bed. However, the Duke and Duchess of York had learned in Ireland that their hosts did not suffer such ailments. When they ate the vegetable pottage set before them they discovered that they felt better. Vegetables were added to the family's diet! Richard and Cecily were able to lay their heads down at night. However, they continued the practice of sleeping under a canopy. This prevented roaches and mice from dropping down upon them from the ceiling at night. Herbs, like lilac and dried flowers hung from the ceiling of the bedroom and other rooms to help cut the smell.

To the west of the castle, the spire of the collegiate church was visible. Edmund had begun the project and now Richard, Duke of York, was completing it. Next to the church was a small village with thatched-roofed cottages, some being larger and more comfortable than others.

As a day's work had become increasingly valuable, life had become somewhat better for peasants. Diets improved but were limited. Peasants ate bacon because it could be salted and preserved, and vegetables that they grew. As bacon and vegetables were the palate of the poor, the majority of the nobility refrained from eating them. If there were others besides the Yorks, who did eat vegetables, it was not made public knowledge.

Giving birth was a delicate matter; many a woman and baby died in the process. Surviving birth, however, was not a guarantee of living to adulthood or even becoming a teenager. One baby in three lived to be a year old. One child in ten celebrated his or her tenth birthday.

Duchess Cicely had already given birth to Anne and Margaret at Fotheringhay. They, like Edward, Edmund, Elizabeth and George, resembled her - blond, tall and beautiful. Edward was a particularly tall, handsome and strapping youth. Cecily had also lost four babies, all of whom resembled her husband — dark and small.

On October 2, 1452, Cecily gave birth to Richard, whose soul had terrible difficulty entering a frail body with his first breath. After some coaxing, Cecily managed to get her infant son to suckle at her own breast, not trusting a wet nurse to save her son. Cecily had nursed George in Ireland; so, breastfeeding was not totally unfamiliar to her. Afterwards, the midwife burped the infant. Cecily fretted! Not even her husband could comfort her.

Cecily pulled herself together when word was brought that Henry VI was planning on stopping at Fotheringhay on his progress. Meals were planned; proper quarters for the King and his company were prepared. The Duke of York had organized a grand reception for Henry, to which neighboring dignitaries and lords were invited. Richard himself greeted his cousin when he disembarked from his royal carriage. Looking a bit bewildered, Henry queried, "Is this London?"

Those who heard, jerked their heads round and paused a moment, but then quietly shrugged off the King's peculiar comment. Mentally they made an excuse for him. After all, Henry may have awoken suddenly from a dream. Richard of York recovered quickly and greeted Henry warmly. "Come and refresh yourself. The Duchess is eager for you to meet our new son."

Henry sat next to the Duke while partaking of light refreshment consisting of twelve courses of various meat dishes. The feast and festivities were planned for later. It was during their conversation when York noticed that the King stopped speaking occasionally in mid-sentence. The Duke waved this off as well. Perhaps, the King had not slept well or the journey had been particularly arduous?

Afterwards, Cecily welcomed Henry and introduced him to her undersized baby, who was still engaged in a battle for his life. Henry gingerly held the infant and remarked, "Your first son!   Well done!"   The Duke and Duchess, dumbfounded, only glanced at one another. Neither one corrected the King.

The medieval world ached for change! The Black Plague had already altered the European social landscape. The Great Dramatist was brewing up other changes as well. German printers invented movable type, making books easier to reproduce. Books were thus more affordable and accessible, encouraging people to learn to read. Three other male babies, who would alter the European consciousness of the world, were born close to Richard's birth - Ferdinand of Aragon, Christopher Columbus and Leonardo da Vinci.

The year following Richard's birth, three events proved to have major importance. The first happened on July 17, when old John Talbot, the Terror of the French, was killed at the Battle of Castillon.   The French also defeated Talbot's army, the last English force in France.   To the utter mortification of the English, Bordeaux fell and Guyenne recognized Charles VII as its sovereign.   Only Calais and the Channel Islands remained under English control. The Hundred Years War had ended after 116 years of vicious fighting and brutal occupation. Disbanded English soldiers returned home; many were unable to find work in the suffering English economy.   Former militia banded together, wandering and menacing the countryside.   King Henry and Queen Margaret were held solely accountable for the loss of French territory and the ensuing disorder.

At the time, the second event seemed of little consequence.   The kindly Henry VI recognized his three bastard half-brothers. Jasper Tudor was created Earl of Pembroke and Edmund the Earl of Richmond; they were both brought to court.   Owen Tudor suffered from the

madness of his grandfather, Charles IV. Henry
paid a considerable sum so that Owen might live
out his days peacefully in a monastery.

The third event occurred in August, when
Henry VI, like Charles IV and Owen Tudor, went
completely and utterly mad. Even Queen Margaret
was unable to hide the King's madness. Looking
out with a blank stare, Henry was unable to
communicate in any fashion whatsoever. Insanity
left the monarch perpetually dumbfounded. In
October, Queen Margaret gave birth to a son. It
had long been rumored that the King had never
pressed for his husbandly rights. Gossip persisted
that young Prince Edward's father was someone
other than King Henry. Most bets went to James,
Earl of Wiltshire, but even though Somerset spent
much of his time in Calais, he was not out of the
running.

Prior to Christmas, the Queen was forced to
summon the Great Council, which immediately
accepted York as its head. Somerset was arrested
in the Queen's chambers. Margaret was infuriated!
After sending Somerset to the White Tower of
London, York assembled the nobility, who swore an
oath of allegiance to Prince Edward. York was
appointed Protector and Defender of the Realm in
the spring of 1454, and given full powers as
Regent. During his short term of office, York
managed to quell the worst of England's growing
problems.

At Christmas, Henry VI regained his sanity.
When Margaret presented the young prince to Henry,
he threw up his hands in utter amazement saying,
"This child must be the son of the Holy Ghost!"
News of Henry's comment spread rapidly,
reinforcing rumors already circulating that the
Prince was illegitimate.

Back in control again, Margaret soon secured
Somerset's release from prison. He was given back

his title of Captain of Calais. The Duke of York left London for Yorkshire and Sandal Castle.

No Yorkist was invited to the Great Council, which Margaret and Somerset called in May 1455. Nobles were being assembled at Leicester for the purpose of defending the King against his enemies. Who were the King's enemies? It didn't take long for the Yorks to ascertain that they were the foes. The Duke of York along with his brother-in-law, the Earl of Salisbury, and the Earl's son, the Earl of Warwick, marched south with their respective armies. They encountered the King's forces at St. Albans where York's forces prevailed after only an hour. Somerset, along with Northumberland and Lord Clifford, the eldest son of Buckingham, were slain in battle. The Duke of Buckingham and the Earls of Dorset and Devon were wounded and taken prisoner. Wiltshire abandoned the field. Henry VI endured a minor wound from an arrow; he was easily captured and courteously returned to London. It was not a revolution! The victor's demands concerned reforms!

In 1456, Gutenberg printed the first Bible, but it was a significant year for a far different reason. Margaret Beaufort, granddaughter and sole heir of the Earl of Somerset, married Edmund Tudor, the Earl of Richmond. She was a pious, impassioned, intelligent thirteen-year-old and very much infatuated. Love, however, was not to last! Edmund Tudor was taken prisoner during the War of the Roses and incarcerated at Carmarthen Castle.

Prison cells were underground dark holes in Norman castles. Oftentimes, prisoners were forgotten altogether. Water might be had from licking a moist stone! Under the circumstances, not long after his incarceration, Edmund died. His widow was seven months pregnant. Margaret anguished over losing the love of her life. Her sorrow turned to wrath and she prayed in desperation for a son. On January 28, 1457, her earnest petitions were answered. Henry Tudor was born at Pembroke Castle under the protection of his uncle, Jasper Tudor, who himself was childless. From that day onwards, Margaret groomed her son for the throne of England. There was no question in her mind that Henry would one day be King of England and she took whatever opportunity she had to impress it firmly upon his mind. She called him her prince and told him tales of how he would one day defeat the nasty Yorks.

That same year, the Queen recovered from her defeat and brought the Court and King back under her power. Margaret's thirst for revenge against York made resolution impossible. Compromise through reconciliation was absent from Margaret's vocabulary. Margaret divided the country into two distinctly different camps by inspiring a habitual state of feuding amongst the nobility. York did not wish to be the antagonist; he realized that public sympathy would not be with him if he took the initiative. However, the Duke was fully aware that in order to bring justice and peace back to England, the Queen must be defeated. York retired to his estates, watching and waiting for the wheel of fortune to take its next spin.

During his first year, Richard struggled to hold onto a thread of life. When he at last reached his first birthday, York considered the possibility that his youngest son, though slight, possessed the same inner strength as his brothers, Edward and Edmund. The Duke contemplated, "It was fitting that his only son born in England should survive."

As was the English custom, thirteen-year-old Anne and eight-year-old Elizabeth had been sent off to be educated in the homes of other nobility.

The rest of Europe saw this practice as a strange, mean-spirited convention. It wasn't out of callousness that this custom prevailed, rather, obedience was expected of both wives and children. The English found it easier to maintain discipline with other people's children than their own. Edward and Edmund were receiving their scholarly education and military training in the warrior code of chivalry at Ludlow Castle. Only six-year old Margaret and George, three years older than Richard, remained at Fotheringhay as his playmates.

While in residence at Fotheringhay, the Duke was often preoccupied with running his estates and conferring with friends and associates. The Duchess supervised the heads of the various households and managed the social calendar. When the Duke and Duchess left to take residence at Ludlow, Sandal or Wigmore, the household goods and castle furniture moved with them.

Depending upon where they were going and what the occasion was, oftentimes, the three youngest children were left behind in the hands of tutors and servants. Childhood memories included standing in the courtyard and looking up to watch the backsides of their parents, soldiers and officers of the household leave by horseback and carriage. The last things the children saw going across the drawbridge were the large wheels of the final wagon.

Only a small staff was left behind. The bustle and hubbub of the castle quieted. The whole structure took on a contemplative character, as if the stones themselves were remembering long held secrets. It was at this time that forgotten memories and ghosts were more accessible. If one had extraordinary abilities and knowledge of the passage of entry, one might enter into the Otherworld of spirit.

As Richard outgrew his nurse, Margaret assumed the role of mother to him, though she preferred George, who was closer to her age. Margaret, fashionably blond and pretty, adored her mother and found it easy to see why her father loved his Duchess. Margaret didn't mind having the responsibility of keeping an eye on Richard. It was a convenient excuse for her to remain at Fotheringhay, rather than trudge off to another noble household.

George was the golden-haired, silver-tongued, even-tempered boy who could be counted upon for a quick gibe and an effortless smile. He was popular, even with those who were older, and made friends easily. The Duke was convinced that George had brought the Irish charm back with him to England. Richard revered his brother and was delighted whenever George put his arm around him or granted him a grin.

When the Duke and Duchess were in residence at Fotheringhay, mother could be expected to drop in unexpectedly to check on the children. When she was able to pull herself away, she took care to give her attention and love equally. The children absorbed her kindness and love. Cecily was never quite sure if her children each felt that he or she was the favorite, or if they all felt that the other was preferred. As long as they were in agreement, Cecily knew that she was keeping things fair. When Richard was three, his mother gave birth for the last time. The infant was stillborn; the soul was unable to enter the tiny physical form. The possibility for life failed to materialize.

Whenever father came by to see the children it was usually in the evening after dinner, if there was no planned entertainment, or Cecily and her ladies were involved with charity projects. Her favorite charities were the convents and monasteries. The Duke brought the children news of their elder brothers, Edward and Edmund, their academic achievements, athletic skills and accomplishments. Father was easily persuaded to recount stories of the battles he had waged, instilling in his sons the virtues of gallantry and honor. He also infused the sense of loyalty to family and an ardent love for justice.

"Are you ever afraid in battle, father?" George once asked.

"Everyone is afraid and a man would be lying if he told you otherwise. The trick is to not dwell on fear but go through it, as suddenly and smoothly as if you were thrusting your sword into a mound of straw. If you do this, my sons, you find exhilaration. It is this exceptional thrill that sees a soldier through a day's battle."

Their father's words emblazoned upon the boys' hearts and minds. After he left, George and Richard took up their wooden swords, playing out the battle script with phantom warriors. Margaret quietly retired close to the fireplace with her embroidery.

Richard had reddish brown hair, and his father's firm jaw and sculptured straightforward features; he had his mother's light blue eyes. Like his father, Richard had little desire for sweets; unlike his father's stocky frame, Richard's was lean and wiry. The years had brought him increasing strength and flexibility, but not breadth to his carriage. His strength came from within. Like other individuals, who put up an extraordinary effort to overcome an uncommonly difficult life situation but left without scars of bitterness, Richard seemingly had boundless energy. Though Richard was small, he had a resolution of spirit to live.

Father once pointed out to Richard the leader of his herd. "It's not always the biggest horse that dominates the herd. That white horse over there bosses the others."

"Why do they let him do that?"

"Because the other horses respect him!" The Duke dwelled momentarily. "Caspian has a driving force! He is my best charger!"

"Why must there be a leader?"

"It is the way of the herd and of civilized men. With the right leader, the rest are protected and prosper. Every soul has a place, be it in a herd or in society, and each place is important and deserves respect."

Richard's arms and legs were slender. He was average height; however, standing next to George dwarfed any child. George easily subdued his younger brother when they wrestled, but he was quietly amazed at the strength Richard was able to muster.

The children had a seesaw and swings, and when their studies were completed, they preferred to play outdoors if weather permitted. Life was uncomplicated! Margaret particularly loved skipping and swinging. George often showed the way in follow-the-leader and when he wasn't the leader his satirical remarks or joking manner focused the attention back onto himself. Richard did not mind in the least, he was always elated to be included and accepted.

Playing hide and seek was infinitely easier when father and mother were away; fewer people to avoid and annoy, and more places to hide. It was on one of these occasions that Richard had chosen a particularly bad place to hide, behind a large pillar. Surely, Margaret would find him in no time. The dark entry allowed in some light; if Margaret approached and he tried to move around the pillar, she would see his shadow on the stone flags. His choice was equally unwise because while he contemplated, he was not paying attention. Margaret surprised him. Looking to his left, Richard saw Margaret's silhouette in the entranceway walking directly towards him. Surely, she must have seen him standing against the side of the column, but Richard thought it was too late to move. She would see his movement if she hadn't already spied him. Richard's breath slowed. He leaned against the cold stone imagining that his body was aligned with the stone. Watching and waiting, Richard wondered what Margaret would do. Margaret continued walking towards his pillar. She paused, not far from where he stood. Glancing around, she seemed to look right through him. She then continued her search.

Later, George asked him, "Where were you hiding?"

Richard recounted his tale and added, "Why she didn't see me?"

George listened with amazement to his younger brother. George paused and laughed. "It's all right if you don't want to reveal your best hiding place. I'll find it eventually!"

"But it really did happen!"

"It's all right little brother, it'll be our secret that you imagined yourself to be invisible!" With that, George put his arm around Richard. Richard basked in the attention, inhaling the love from George. His young heart swelled with love for his older brother.

For the most part, the boys rode their ponies on the grassy unfortified half of the island with the Master of the Horses, a soldier or groom in attendance. At first, Richard found trotting particularly bumpy. "Keep your weight in your stirrups and your heels down!" a groom advised. Richard followed instructions and while it was helpful, it still wasn't quiet right. He was still bouncing!

On his next riding lesson, it was the Master of the Horses, who suggested, "Feel your pony underneath you. Instead of trying to grip with legs or knees, try moving with your horse. Become a moving object on another moving object!"

"How?"

"Your weight is in the balls of your feet as if you were standing! Your heels are down! Good! At the same time, keep your seat bones on the saddle, as if they were attached." The Master of the Horses assessed the situation. "Let's lengthen your stirrups a little so that your legs are straighter. In this way, you won't be sitting back as if you were on a chair."

The adjustment changed Richard's posture. He moved further up to the front of the saddle. "Is this right?"

Richard had his weight in his stirrups as if he were standing on the ground. "Good! Now when your horse walks, keep your weight in your stirrups and your seat bones on the saddle. At the same time, let your seat follow the pony's movement." When Richard was able to follow his pony's movement at the walk, the Master of the Horses proceeded with trotting instructions. "When your pony trots, his movement is more rapid. his legs come up higher and it is more difficult for you to stay in the saddle. So, what you want to do is let the movement of the pony come up through you. First through one leg and down the other, then through the other leg. Back and forth without pause! Don't tighten your seat! Let the cheeks in your seat go back and forth with the movement of the trot. Let the pony move you!"

It took a bit of persuading for Richard to get his pony from walking along comfortably to trotting ahead. When the pony started out trotting slowly, it was easier to follow the Master of the Horses' instructions. When the pony's trot became more aggressive, it was more difficult. "Sir, what do I do?"

The Master of the Horses sent for a length of rope and when the soldier returned with it, the Master of the Horses secured one end to the pony's bridle. The Master of the Horses backed up and sent the pony off in a circle around him. "Let's try it again! When you lose your connection, we'll bring the pony back to a walk and then try again.

Richard concentrated! He felt the energy of the horse coming up through his left foot, up his left leg, across his hips, down his right leg and out his right foot. As the energy exited his right foot, new energy from the pony came into his right foot in the same manner. The Master of the Horses called out, "Good! Sit up tall and straight! Keep your shoulders back and down! Chest up! Don't clutch your stomach in — it pushes your shoulders down and forwards! Keep your hands quiet and look up!" It was a lot for a young boy to remember!

A soldier came out from the gatehouse. He worked his way to the center of the circle and spoke with the Master of the Horses. The Master of the Horses turned back to Richard. "Good job! Walk your ponies out, boys. This man will help you!"

Richard looked over at George, "Why do we walk our ponies out?"

"They can get sick if they are put away hot and sweaty." George rewarded Richard with one of his famous smiles. "Say, you did very well out there today!"

Richard beamed and then told George about the energy he had experienced. George knitted his brow, "I wouldn't be telling other people about this. Don't worry, I'll keep your secret." George looked over at the restless soldier, who would voice disapproval if he asked his pony to trot out just then.

The next time the boys were out riding, George tried feeling the energy surges from one leg to the other when he trotted. While he was unable to feel the energy of his pony coming into his feet, George was able to relax and feel the movement. In this way, he was naturally able to move his legs with the horse. The ride became smoother and George's pony changed his high head carriage to one of a relaxed arched neck. This time while they were cooling out their ponies, it was George who looked over at Richard. "You're a pretty nice little brother to have!" Richard knew in his heart that this is what heaven must feel like.

With practice, Richard was able to keep his weight in the stirrups. This stopped him from gripping with his knees or legs. When he was able to relax his legs, the saddle filled up between his thighs. He was able to rest his calves against the sides of his pony. In this way, when he applied pressed with his calves, the pony was more responsive. Richard talked to George about riding but did not mention the pony's energy again.

A bond of friendship and love grew between the brothers. Richard idolized his older brother; George less frequently made an outward display of his affection. Life was good, but childhood was about to end abruptly, as it too often did in the 15th century.

In 1457, Queen Margaret's friend, General Piers de Breze, sailed to the English coast and burned Sandwich. Public animosity towards the detested Queen reached a fever pitch. Only the Lancastrian lords, who reaped the benefits from Henry's incompetence, supported the Queen. Ballads were sung of Queen Margaret's infamy and went on to question who the Prince's real father might be. At best Queen Margaret was a public joke. Fearing outright rebellion, the Queen's government was forced to yield to public demand. Warwick had been made Captain of Calais after

Somerset's death. Queen Margaret was now forced to give the popular Warwick a three-year naval commission to protect the sea. Soon afterwards, Warwick's heroic acts in the Channels gave the English a reason to be proud.

By the spring of 1459, the Queen's unquenched craving for vengeance led to preparations for war against the Yorks and their allies. Every one of York's allies had their own particular reasons for being discontented with the Queen and her court. Fotheringhay was no longer a safe haven. The Duke made preparations for Cecily, six-year-old Richard and ten-year-old George to travel from the Scottish boarder, through the West Midlands to the refuge of Ludlow Castle on the Welsh Marches. It would be a long, arduous journey, as they would have to avoid Lancastrians along the way. Gentry and nobles, who were friendly to the Yorkist cause, would provide safe shelter at night.

Margaret was to be discretely escorted, to the household of neighboring gentry, where she would be safe. Lachrymose, Margaret did not want to leave her mother. Cecily comforted her daughter. "You will be protected. The Queen's heart is not so black that she has turned against little girls."

"But what of you and father?

"Don't be frightened! Your father is indomitable. He will keep his family safe." Cecily took her daughter's hand. "Remember the stories your father told you? How could he not succeed?" Cecily brushed her daughter's blond hair off her brow and kissed her gently. "Be a good girl! I will send for you when I am able."

Cecily watched her daughter's coach leave and returned to supervise the preparations. She was in her mid-forties. Though strands of white hair were intermittently dispersed through her flaxen hair, she was still admired for her beauty.

Early in her marriage, she had one indiscretion. Afterwards, she remained loyal, setting her mind and will to the duties of her peerage and family. Cecily had accompanied her husband on the perilous route to and from Ireland. She'd observed firsthand, how through wit, cunning and luck the Duke had brought them through safely. This journey to Ludlow was different. Queen Margaret had escalated a disagreement into civil war. Cecily worried!

At last, the porters had finished loading the wagons, the carriage had been prepared and the soldiers were mounted and armed. The boys were escorted to the coach by their tutor. He offered Cecily a hand into the carriage and then lifted six-year old Richard so that he sat next to George.

Cecily smiled down at her two serious boys. "You will be meeting your older brothers soon."

Heavily guarded, the party left the flatlands behind, venturing into the vast forests. The canopy provided by the immense oaks, chestnuts and elms allowed only flickering, dancing lights onto the riders and wagons. The woods had its symphony. The screech of a hawk, chattering and whistling of smaller birds, howls from a distant wolf pack and nearby rustling of a larger, unseen animal harrowed from a midday slumber lumbered off snapping dried fallen branches underfoot. The sounds of men disturbed the woodland inhabitants. Grinding of creaking wheels, the predictable clip clopping of hoofs and the occasional horse snort were familiar, dangerous sounds to the creatures of the forest.

Roads were rough. Soldiers regularly stopped to clear the way of large branches and even on occasion, fallen trees. Reaching the rolling hills of the Midlands, scouts were dispatched to check for possible ambushes. Each time the men returned, the route was either confirmed, or if a detour was planned, the party set off quietly. George grinned. Leaning over, he whispered in Richard's ear, "Now would be a good time to make yourself, as well as the rest of us, invisible."

Richard was a bit taken aback, surprised that his brother remembered. "Really?"

George rubbed the top of Richard's head and smiled, "I'm just teasing you."

Richard was undeterred by George's last comment. With the hope that he might make a difference, Richard tried to remember what it felt like to be a part of his surroundings and for the next several miles he tried concentrating. It took well over an hour for George to realize what his younger brother was up to. When he did, George roared with laughter, "I can still see you, Richard!"

Richard looked up at George sheepishly. Cecily was taken aback! Ever so slightly, she turned her head, knitted her brows and asked, "Boys! What is going through those heads of yours this time?"

George roared with laughter, "You'd never guess!"

Richard blushed. Cecily suppressed her laughter. "Richard, if you are helping us, we admire your loyalty."

George rubbed the top of Richard's head. "You are an interesting little brother. All in all, I'd rather have you on my side." The boys took up posts at the carriage windows, keeping an eye out for Ludlow Castle.

Ludlow Castle, a massive defensible fortress, stood on high ground, guarded by both the rivers Tene and Corve, with steep cliffs to the north and west. Built from limestone, quarried from its own site, it was the most strategic fortification on the Welsh boarders. The Norman gatehouse and the battlements on the outer bailey wall were the first glimpses of the castle, the party saw as they rode through the town. The Duke was notified immediately that his wife and younger sons had arrived. He breathed an audible sigh of relief, but the seriousness of the moment yet predominated his typical jovial temperament.

Once through the gatehouse they entered the large, four-acre outer bailey or courtyard. Troupes were trained, exercised and mustered in the outer bailey. Horses were grazed and the stables, workshops, lodgings and storehouses were conveniently located here. The Chapel of St. Peter, built by Roger Mortimer, was to the left.

When the Duke and Duchess were in residence, the grounds swarmed with visiting nobles and officials, priests, monks and friars, chambermaids, cooks, clerks, grooms and farriers, weavers and herbalists, tutors, clerks and porters. Some resided in the castle. Others lived in the nearby village.

Holy days and saints' feast days of the liturgical calendar were celebrated in the outer bailey with jousting tournaments and other competitive entertainment. On May Day, each young maiden chose a knight and crowned him with a rosary of roses. At Christmas the Festival of Fools was held. One jester was chosen to serve as a bogus bishop. He was ordained in ridiculously decorative vestments. To the amusement of the crowds, he delivered his sermon in gibberish and sang boorish songs. Midsummer's Eve and Harvest sported special events particular to the occasion.

The U-shaped Mortimer's Tower was unlike the other square towers. It served as the gatehouse that controlled the rear exit from the Castle. It led to Dirham Bridge, which offered the shortest means to Wigmore and Wales. Mortimer's Tower stood nearly directly across from the party on the western perimeter wall. The party proceeded to the Norman gatehouse guarding the inner bailey.

Above the entrance to the inner bailey was a carved set of arms.

The inner bailey wall was six feet thick, surrounded by a steep ditch cut out from the rock and flanked by four open-backed square towers. These were constructed so that archers would be able to send their arrows into anyone attempting to scale the wall. Upon entering the inner bailey, the round Chapel of Saint Mary Magdalene, constructed in the manner of the Knights Templar, stood in front of the party. Its beautifully carved entrance and decorative work invited penitents and worshipers into the circular nave.

The North Range, directly opposite the gatehouse, was built in a crescent shape. Within its walls could be found the Great Hall, measuring 60 by 30 feet. Tapestries hung on the walls. Rush mats were laid on the floors - stone flags on the ground floor and wooden floorboards on the upper floors. Throughout the year, sweet and pungent herbs were sprinkled on the mats and hung from the ceilings to cut obnoxious orders. All of the mats throughout the castle were removed at the end of May, and replaced by fresh ones.

The kitchen was located within the walls of the North Range. It was busy yearlong, feeding castle residents and preparing feasts for huge banquets. Two of the three fireplaces were large enough to stand in. One measured 16 feet in length and was used to roast meats; large joints and flanks. Whole pigs were secured on spits and turned by young boys. The other fireplace was used for cooking vegetables, pottages and boiling meats.

The bread oven door was held in place with a piece of dough while bread was cooking so that the cook could tell by looking at it when the pastries and breads were ready. Chimneys ran the full height of the North Range wall. The kitchen heat was so intense that only men worked in the kitchen, and they wore little or nothing. Within the walls of the large chimneys were bricks that jutted out and served as footholds so that the chimney sweeps might clean the soot out. A small fireplace provided the pilot fire. Portable charcoal burners were used for frying and grilling.

Meats were butchered and hung in the game room. Open barrels of stone ale, mead and wine were kept in the buttery. The stock was stored in the wine cellar.

Most of the food preparation was carried on at tables in the middle of the kitchen. Assistant cooks helped the head cook and scullions scrubbed the pots and pans. The head cook was in charge of ordering goods and supplies.

The Great Tower faced south. It was a four-storey, tall structure immediately to the west of the gatehouse. It had its own smaller walled courtyard and served as the castle's keep. On the first floor, a two-storey living hall and adjoining bedroom provided quarters for the Duke and Duchess when they were in residence. Interiors were decorated with paneling, plasterwork and large tapestries. Fireplaces in each of the rooms provided warmth. Meals for the family and visiting friends or dignitaries were prepared in a smaller kitchen within the keep. Even though the fortress was in the frontier, Ludlow's keep was warmer than most castles.

The carriage stopped immediately in front of the Great Tower. George and Richard looked out of the carriage in awe. Walking proudly towards them, on either side of their father, were seventeen-year old Edward and sixteen-year old Edmund, both of whom looked like older versions of George — particularly, Edmund. The Duke offered Cecily a hand to get out of the carriage. He kissed her endearingly. The young boys scrambled down after her. York gave each of them a hug.

Stepping back, he stood behind them, placing his hands on their shoulders he spoke. "It's time that you met your older brothers." Nodding to his eldest sons in turn, "Edward and Edmund greet George and Richard." To the younger brothers' eyes, Edward and Edmund had the appearance of grown men. The older brothers reputation had preceded them. They stood taller than most men and were already belted earls.

Cecily poured out her affection to her older sons, who obviously adored her. Then the Duke took his Duchess' hand. "Edward! Edmund! Please see to it that your brothers are fed and they find their sleeping quarters." Richard's smaller hand rested comfortably in Edward's firm grip as they walked into the keep.

While they ate, Edward and Edmund told the stories of battle and defending the family honor that their father had told and retold. George and Richard listened attentively as if they were hearing the adventures for the first time. The older boys explained what life and training was like at Ludlow Castle. Later that evening, George and Richard had difficulty falling asleep. When they fell into a slumber, their dreams were filled with their valiant older brothers — Edward, Earl of March and Edmund, Earl of Rutland.

The following day, Edward and Edmund took the time to show their younger siblings around the castle. They climbed up the narrow, spiral stairs and through a corridor to an empty bedroom. George asked, "Why isn't this being used?"

Edmund smiled, "Because Marion de Bruer threw herself out that window after running a sword through her lover."

George asked, "Why would she want to go and do something as unkind as that?"

"A most handsome, but not chivalrous, knight by the name of Arthur seduced Marion. Then he talked her into helping him escape.'

George smiled, "That was the last she heard of him?"

"Unfortunately, not! Arthur returned to this very keep by following his escape route. The problem was that he brought company with him. Walter de Lacy and his contingent of soldiers slaughtered the entire garrison. When Marion learned of the grisly deed, she killed Arthur and threw herself out the window."

Edward laughed, "Hell knows no wrath comparable to a woman's vengeance."

Edmund continued, "Since then, people have sworn they have seen the specters of the ill-fated lovers. Our unwary chambermaid heard a whisper and turned to find no one. At least no one with a body."

Edward interjected, "The Church does not believe in ghosts."

"My brothers, Ludlow is not the only haunted castle in the realm. If a cold chill passes through you, sending a chill down your spine or your hair to stand on end, you may just have encountered Marion or Arthur."

Edward shook his head. "Never mind Edmund! He gets carried away!"

"Someday, my brother, you may encounter a specter. It will make a believer out of you."

Throughout the summer months, the Duke and his eldest sons met with other Yorkist leaders to formulate strategies and battle plans. Richard was aware of what was transpiring among the adults; however, his major preoccupation was enjoying the sunshine of his older brothers' affection. Though there was tension and concern in the air, all in all, it was the best summer Richard and George had ever experienced. They didn't mind studying with their tutors. In the evening, Edward and Edmund might help them with their lessons. Other evenings, the younger boys sat next to their older brothers while the bards told stories, or the minstrels sang and played songs. Sometimes, Edward, Edmund and William Hastings, Edward's best friend, danced to the music. Then they returned to the young boys, taking them by their hands, encouraging them to move their feet to the rhythm and delight of the tune. The Duke and Duchess of York enjoyed these moments, as the gaiety pressed aside their perilous present circumstances.

When Edward, Edmund and William Hastings exercised and practiced with the soldiers, Richard and George were privileged to serve as grooms. Intermittently during the day, Edward and Edmund paused to show their brothers how to handle their wooden swords, show them exercises to build strength and endurance, or ask them to run an errand. George was every bit as enthusiastic as Richard; however, he often felt that since he was older, his place was with Edward and Edmund, not with Richard.

Like everyone else, Edward found George an easy and likeable companion. Edward also saw in George his own affinity for pleasure and the easy life of the nobility. What Edward found in Richard was their father's sense of fairness, as well as an indomitable nature that they had both inherited from their mother.

York was only moderately aware of the bond of brotherhood growing between his boys. He had more immediate concerns. His preoccupation was with the growing force that Queen Margaret was gathering at Coventry. It consisted of Lancastrians, Welshmen and Scots. When the Queen's spies informed her that the Duchess of York's eldest brother, the Earl of Salisbury, and his son, Richard, Earl of Warwick, were marching towards Ludlow Castle to join the Duke of York, she dispatched Lords Audeley and Dudley to set a trap. Forewarned by his own scouts, Salisbury held his men in the woodlands on higher ground where the density of the trees was such that each of his soldiers would be able to engage the Queen's men one at a time. Salisbury and his troops were badly outnumbered, but his archers were strategically positioned, and his men in arms fought ferociously. At the end of the day, the royal contingent was defeated. Dudley was counted among the slain; Audeley was taken prisoner.

Salisbury and Warwick marched toward Ludlow Castle. Andrew Trollope was among the commanders, leading Warwick's formidable troops from Calais. News of the victory preceded them. York's boys watched from the battlements for signs of their heroic uncle and cousin. At the first sighting of Salisbury and Warwick's fluttering banners, the boys' hearts leapt in their chests with pride. They marked the party's entire coarse across the valley. Waving and cheering excitedly, the boys flew down the steps, across the drawbridge, out the gatehouse and into the town.

On October 12, a royal force nearly twice the size as that of York's, advanced into the valley. With an offer of pardon, Andrew Trollope and the Calais garrison defected, taking with them their knowledge of York's plans. That evening, by torchlight in the Great Chamber, York, Salisbury and Warwick met with their captains. Shadows, larger than the men themselves, waltzed and wavered on the walls. Andrew Trollope's betrayal was a disaster. Fortunately, Trollope was unacquainted of the route from Mortimer's Tower. It was determined that the York leaders and their remaining troops would head for Wales. Once there, York and Rutland would head west, seeking passage to Ireland. Warwick, Salisbury and March were to journey south to Devon and sail to Calais. As speed was of the utmost necessity, it was decided that Cecily, Richard and George would remain behind, placing themselves at the mercy of the court. The Duke assured Cecily, "You and the boys will be safe. The Queen would risk too much if she harmed you or our sons."

George and Richard watched unnoticed in the background. Edward took a moment, walked over to his young brothers and putting his broad hands on their shoulders. "Stand strong when the soldiers enter and go willingly with them to their camp."

"Will mother be all right?" Richard asked.

"All you two have to do is stand your ground. Our King, while incompetent, does have a soft heart. Be brave!"

In the middle of the night, the York men left through the gatehouse at Mortimer's Tower. They left quietly, with the alacrity of a deer being pursued by a pack of gray timber wolves. After their departure, Cecily was unable to sleep. She dismissed her ladies and before dawn, she went to her boys. Gently she shook Richard and George, who had just fallen asleep not many hours before. Groggy, they did not immediately remember their family's turn in circumstances.

"Come boys, we are going to try to prevent mayhem."

"Where are we going?" Asked Richard.

"To the steps of the marker cross in town." She smiled tenderly. "The Queen's captains will see us first. They may just take us back to camp and leave the town be."

"What of the Queen?"

"The Queen is unpopular enough and will not risk harming the three of us."

They walked noiselessly to their destination. Between the two boys existed a tacit contract that they would not let their mother or their family down. Richard and George held tightly onto Cecily's hands. Memories of family valor played across Richard's mind. At the marker cross, his mother's fortitude gave him the strength to be brave.

It started as a game in the mind of a precocious seven-year-old. Richard focused intently on remaining still. After a time, he found himself thinking outside of himself. In his mind he watched the Queen's army enter Ludlow. An angry captain with a slight build brought his horse to a halt in front of the Duchess, George and himself. Then the captain ordered several of his men to escort them to a nearby wagon. With a start, Richard came back to himself. He wondered what George was thinking. Richard turned his attention to the ground beneath his feet, so that he might stand his ground when the soldiers arrived.

All thoughts were interrupted by the sounds of the early morning hustle of the Queen's army in the near distance making ready to march on Ludlow. The first light of the new day brought with it the resonance of the chargers heavy hoofs on firm ground, the clamor of armor and, now and again, the shout of a captain reorganizing his command. Cecily and the boys had waited dauntlessly for nearly three hours for the royal banners to emerge from the woodlands heralding the King's regiments. Richard remembered Edward's words and glanced fleetingly to George, who had taken a firm stance. Richard copied his older brother's posture and imagined that he was propping his mother up.

Sounds of the marching army came closer. They come into view. Primed for battle, the soldiers were thwarted to find their quarry gone. As Richard had seen in his mind, his mother, George and himself were taken immediately to the royal camp. Surprisingly, the captain resembled the man in his daydream. No sooner had the wagons left the outreaches of Ludlow, than the sacking of the town commenced, as if it were in a foreign, hostile land. Drunken soldiers stripped the castle to the bare walls. They did, however, remember to free Audeley and the other prisoners from Ludlow's prison.

King Henry placed Cecily, Richard and George in the custody of her sister, the Duchess of Buckingham, who continuously berated Cecily for the Duke of York's insurrection. Always a kindly man, Henry granted Cecily a thousand marks a year to maintain herself and her sons. Henry could afford to be generous; the Crown confiscated the properties of York, Salisbury and Warwick.

From Calais, Edward, Earl of March, sent a request to Thomas Bourgchier, Archbishop of Canterbury, asking him to take Richard and George into his household. The pious King offered no objections. When his mother brought him the news, Richard wondered at how his brother was able to watch out for him from so far away.

Richard and George had both heard about Canterbury. Canterbury was the most popular shrine in England, nay, all of Europe. Its importance as a major pilgrim destination dated back to 1170. Thomas Becket, Archbishop of Canterbury, had been Henry II's friend and protégé, but Henry discovered too late that Becket had a backbone. Becket refused to allow the Church, her property and riches to be subordinate to Henry II's control. After years of struggle between the two men, Henry II publicly proclaimed, "Will no one rid me of this low-born cleric?"

Four knights, loyal to the King, took up the challenge. They made no secret of their intent to kill Becket. The Archbishop was warned, but he preferred to face the inevitable in the sanctuary of Canterbury Cathedral, rather than be killed in some obscure location. On December 29, 1170, the knights arrived at the cathedral. When Becket refused to leave they tried unsuccessfully to manhandle him. Richard de Brito dealt the fatal blow by slicing off the top of Becket's head with his sword. Shock and horror reverberated throughout England and the Continent. Henry II was forced to have the knights executed, but that was not enough! Henry relinquished all attempts to subjugate the Church to the State's authority. That was not enough! Three and a half years after Becket's death, Henry II was compelled by Pope Alexander III to do penance. Henry showed up at the Cathedral shoeless and wearing sackcloth, to be flogged next to Becket's casket.

Immediately after Thomas Becket's death, miracles began to occur for those who prayed at Becket's coffin, located in a crypt in the basement. Unexplainable wonders and healings led to Becket's canonization on February 21, 1173. Pilgrims from all over Europe prayed at Canterbury for Saint Thomas Becket's intervention. They left donations, amounting from a few simple coins to exquisite jewels, jewelry and gold. Canterbury's pilgrim traffic superseded that of Winchester Cathedral where the shrine of Saint Swithun and the tomb of Alfred the Great resided.

In 1220, Becket's remains were ceremoniously moved up to the ground floor of the Cathedral. Behind the high altar a gorgeously prepared tomb had been prepared. It was there that Becket's last resting place prevailed in spite of the fact that more miracles occurred when his remains were in the basement.

Canterbury Cathedral was magnificent. Eight large supporting columns in the basement were repeated on the ground floor. Pilgrims were able to contemplate the stained glass windows commemorating Thomas Becket's life and martyrdom while waiting their turn to pray near the high altar. All in all, the effect was a marketing marvel!

Under the tutelage of the Archbishop, the boys immediately took up their books and resumed their studies. Richard, like Edward, was particularly bright. Scholarly tasks at Canterbury included reading and speaking Latin, reading classics and writing Italic script. Sometimes, when they were alone, they read books on chivalry. The British believed that in the distant past, their ancestors were better off than they were. Thus, romance became an entwined facet of history.

George and Richard lived in an age when bards told and retold stories of King Arthur and his Round Table. Chivalry and honor, dying bravely and a man's word were the central keys to identity both in this world and the next. Along with King Arthur, Saint George personified the values of the Knights of the Round Table.

Though St. George never made it to the British Isles, he had become a popular cult hero in Western Europe. He was a military saint, who devotedly made the sign of the cross before slaying dragons. Afterwards, he spread the good news of Christ's teachings. However, St. George lived during the Roman persecutions of the Christians. After surviving several attempts on his life, which included being thrown into a cauldron of molten lead, he converted those who would have martyred him.

George managed to borrow a copy of Geoffrey of Monmouth's *Exploits of King Arthur,* which had been translated into classical Latin verse. Because it was written in classical Latin verse, the Archbishop approved the reading selection. However, the boys must complete their other work first.

Hurriedly, the boys finished their studies. Richard settled back, impatiently waiting for George to read about the bravest of youths and greatest of kings. As George began, Richard moved to the edge of his seat, eagerly listening to how young Arthur pulled the enchanted Excalibur from its stony incarceration, authorizing Arthur to be the true and rightful ruler. Hero knights fought black knights in mortal combat! Lancelot's courage, skills and warrior code mandated that he must fight at least four men at once; otherwise, the engagement would be an unfair contest! Merlin's intervention and magical happenings caused Richard's young mind to wonder what life would be like if real magic did exist.

George used his charm to borrow a copy of John of Glastonbury's tale of King Arthur. In the twelfth century, monks discovered the tomb of King Arthur at the Abbey. In the thirteenth century, a monk by the name of John of Glastonbury wrote the story that had evolved through the years, as to how Joseph of Arimathea brought the Holy Grail to Glastonbury and then to King Arthur's court. The monks wisely never claimed to possess the Grail, but people suspected that it was in the monks' possession. Pilgrims visited the crypt in the Lady Chapel, asking St. Joseph of Arimathea to intervene on their behalf to the Almighty.

The Archbishop had his own particular reading favorites. He saw to it that these were also included in the boys' curriculum. *Beowulf* was a special favorite of the Archbishop's. It was an Anglo-Saxon poem, written for the royal court in East Anglia. George and Richard both enjoyed the Archbishop's choice. Disturbing thought it was that the monster Grendel and the dragon defeated the hero in the land of Greats. Comforting that Beowulf's heroism and honor survived him beyond the grave.

Then twelve brave warriors, sons of heroes
Rode round the barrow, sorrowing,
They mourned their king, chanted
An elegy, spoke about the great man.
They exalted his heroic life, lauded
His daring deeds; it is fitting for a man,

When his lord and friend must leave this life,
To mouth words in his praise
And to cherish his memory.
Thus the Geats, his hearth-companions,
Grieved over the death of their lord,
They said that of all kings on earth
He was the kindest, the most gentle,
The most just to his people,
            the most eager for fame.

Richard enjoyed all of his studies. He loved music and liked playing the lute. When he was studying, his young mind was compelled to concentrate on something other than his family's turn of fortune. Sometimes when he was alone, he played the military strategies that had been used by both sides in his head, or worked them out on the ground with pretend soldiers in mock battles. He used common objects for center, right and left flanks, for enemies, castles, rivers and countless determiners of the outcome of battle.

Life was better at Canterbury than at Buckingham's manor. Both boys were encouraged by the Archbishop not to worry. "It's not over yet, boys and all of England knows it." Daily, the boys went to hear the Archbishop say mass where, behind him, laid the remains of Thomas Becket. The boys prayed with all of their hearts for Saint Thomas Becket to intervene. Many in England, on both sides of the controversy did as well, or went directly to the Source, invoking God Himself to prevail on behalf of their petitions.

God the Father Almighty hears all prayers and answers them within the limits of the Spirit of the Times! Spring yielded to summer! Apprehension mounted! The King and Queen fretfully stirred about the Midlands awaiting the inevitable invasion.

Father of Kings

Dubliners heartily welcomed Edmund, Earl of Rutland, and the Duke of York, who was recognized as Britain's ruler by both the Irish Parliament and populace. English messengers, delivering orders demanding York's arrest or demise, were themselves taken and executed. Meanwhile, Salisbury, Warwick and March landed in Calais, where they received a warm welcome from Salisbury's brother, the governor. Also lending their support to the Yorkist cause was the Merchants of the Staple. It had grown into the most influential financial organization in all of England and was still headquartered in Calais.

While Salisbury and March drummed up support, Warwick looked to the sea. On January 7, 1460, he surprised Lord Rivers and his son, Sir Anthony Woodville, at Sandwich, where they had been preparing to attack Calais. Early in April, Warwick sailed to Ireland where he met with York and Rutland to finalize plans for the invasion.

In late June, Salisbury, Warwick and March returned to England with two thousand men. Men joined their ranks eagerly, as they marched to London. The city's gates were opened to them; London was theirs with the exception of the Tower.

Turning their army north, on July 10th, they encountered the royal army commanded by the Duke of Buckingham in mud up to their knees at the River Nene. This time, the wheel of fortune smiled upon the Yorkist faction; an entire wing of the King's army joined the Yorkist cause. The ensuing battle lasted for nearly an hour; in the end, Buckingham, Beaumont, Egremont and Shrewsbury were dead. King Henry VI was captured and the royal forces defeated. On July 16th they returned to London with Henry VI, as their royal prize, to establish a workable, honest government.

On September 15th, Cecily, with her three youngest children, arrived in London. She left Richard, George and Margaret under the protection of Edward, in order that she might join up with her husband in Chester. Though Edward was much sought after, he took time everyday to visit his siblings, showering them with brotherly love. To the delight of George and Richard, Edward told them about his hazardous flight from Ludlow Castle and gave a detailed, blow-by-blow description of the battle at River Nene.

Edward's presence commanded attention. He stood over six feet tall, was extremely handsome and had a magnificent carriage. His easygoing way with everyone, regardless of their station, won him friends and admirers. His passion for life was catching. Edward's excellent memory included a knack for remembering the names of everyone he met — peers, gentry and commoners. Where in any tale of chivalry was there a hero to match Edward?

Richard was eight the day the Duke of York triumphantly entered London to cheering throngs and a trumpet fanfare. York was considered by one and all a reformer. However, he had had his fill of the Queen and empty promises. Without warning, the Duke of York laid claim to the throne! Peers, including his eldest sons and Warwick, were dismayed. York was the wrong man, in the wrong place, at the wrong hour. Parliament settled on a compromise. York was declared Henry's heir and Prince Edward was disinherited. That is, except in the minds of the Lancastrians and Queen Margaret.

Stubbornly, Queen Margaret was not about to give in. Fleeing to Scotland, she secretly proceeded to gather forces from the north around her at Hull. Spies brought news of the Queen's endeavors to London! In response to the danger, York divided his troops. While Warwick remained in London to guard the city, Edward headed to Wales with one army. York, Salisbury and Edmund marched to Yorkshire with a second army.

December 21, 1460, found York at Sandal Castle; the Queen's forces held nearby Pontefract Castle. Both agreed to a Christmas truce. On December 30th, the Lancastrians placed honor and rules of engagement aside by attacking a contingent of York's troops outside Sandal's battlements. York, Salisbury and Rutland bravely rushed out to support their comrades. They were easily outmaneuvered, outnumbered, surrounded and trounced! York was slain! Lord Clifford caught up with Edmund, who begged for mercy. Clifford had none to give. "By God's blood, your father slew mine and I shall do the same to you!"

Salisbury was captured and beheaded. His head along with those of York's and Edmund's were impaled on the gates of the city of York. A mock crown of paper and straw was wedged on the Duke's head.

Margaret was elated but her victory was not complete — London and the King were in the hands of her enemies. She turned her forces south. Full-scale war resumed! Paupers and beggars ran with the Queen's army. Like a swarm of locusts over the land; they burned, pillaged and raped their way to London. Margaret had overstepped the boundaries, losing the support of the kingmakers!

Early in February 1461, through superior generalship, Edward and his forces crushed Jasper Tudor's army at the battle of Mortimer's Cross in Wales. Jasper escaped but his father, Owen Tudor, was taken prisoner and sentenced to death. Before the headsman did his work, Owen had a few last words. "This head that once lay in Queen Catherine's lap will soon be on the stock. I put my heart and mind wholly unto God." Afterwards, Owen Tudor's head was set on the market cross. A mad woman came to attend to it. Combing his hair and washing off the blood, she set a circle of lit candles around it.

Warwick left London with Henry VI and a small army. At St. Albans it was the Queens turn! Her forces all at once attacked Warwick's flank. Warwick's left wing crumbled! With his army scattered, Warwick headed west with what remained of his forces to join Edward. After the battle, Margaret discovered Henry under a tree laughing and talking to unseen entities he called angels.

All of London was in a state of panic with the news of the Queen's approaching forces. Merchants and Londoners hid their valuables. Men armed themselves with clubs and pitchforks. Ships in the harbor hoisted sail. Cecily and her three youngest children were back on board one of them. She was setting sail for the Low Countries, having just lost a husband, a brother and a son.

Cecily's initial reception was respectful but chilly. They were quietly escorted to Utrecht. Duke Philip of Burgundy, a Renaissance man before his time, wisely waited to see who would emerge as the English victor. Duke Philip traced his ancestry back to John of Gaunt and favored the Lancasters over the Yorks. However, Burgundy was too small to be caught on the wrong side of an English civil war. He could not risk inadvertently aggravating the victor.

London was the Queen's for the taking but Margaret hesitated. All of her efforts had been on behalf of her young son. If her forces sacked London, would the populace ever accept Prince Henry as king? However, as Yorkist support was in London, if her army did not control the city, it would be more difficult to face the Duke's son, Edward and Warwick. Dilemmas threw Margaret off balance. She was effective when presented with one coarse of action, especially if it was generated by strong emotions. Ten days later, the choice was no longer hers to make. Edward seized the moment, hastening back to London with Warwick and their men. Londoners proclaimed Edward the savior of the city. The Queen retreated northward.

Edward's entrance into London was staged like a Christmas pageant. Warwick and an inner circle of Yorkist leaders had met at Baynard's Castle earlier, where they predetermined that Edward would be England's next king. The destruction Margaret's army had caused to the property of gentry and peers was unacceptable!

At St. John's Field, Warwick cried out to the crowds, "Is Henry still worthy to reign as King?"

In unison people repeatedly shouted, "No!"

"Will you have the Earl of March as your King?"

A deafening roar rose from the people, yelling again and again, "Yes! Yes! Yes!"

On March 4, Edward sat in the king's see at Westminster, holding Saint Edward's scepter.

One week later, Edward and Warwick set out after the Queen's forces. They were determined to end the strife that held England gridlocked. On Palm Sunday, in a blinding snowstorm at Towton, Edward found his target. Though badly outnumbered, Edward laid out a successful battle plan. A raging battle commenced at sunrise and concluded at ten o'clock in the evening. Vanquished Lancastrians were pursued and cut down as unmercifully as Edmund had been slain. At the end of the day, some 28,000 bodies lay scattered over miles of terrain.

Despite the cold, a reek of death hung heavily over the land. Some souls had little difficulty finding their way to the Light, while others did not know they were dead. Memory of the violence reverberated into the earth like a silent echo. The old King and Queen, along with the former Prince Edward, sought asylum in Scotland.

On his journey back to London, Edward and his men stopped at the manor of Lord Rivers. Rivers' son, Anthony Woodville, had just fought for Henry at Towton and was one of the few who managed to escape. Edward wanted to size up the situation. Was it possible for Lord Rivers to support the new government, which Edward now headed? It was in England's best interest to bring peace and bestow mercy wherever it could be mandated. Edward's government required good men, who were willing to switch their loyalties.

Among those who scrambled to greet the new King and victor of Towton was Lord Rivers' twenty-five year old daughter, Elizabeth. Many considered her to be the greatest beauty in all of England - nay, all of Europe! Edward loved beautiful things and was immediately drawn to her. William Hastings sized up the situation immediately, determining that the troops would be camping on Lord River's manor for the night.

Edward had pursued and won many a lady at court, but he never forced himself upon a woman. As for Elizabeth, humility was not in her nature. She had no intention of becoming one of Edward's flings and, so, she refused his fervent advances. Elizabeth was more than five years older than Edward. She was the widow of Sir John Grey, Lord Ferres, who had been killed by the York's forces at St. Albans. Elizabeth did leave an impression upon Edward. Several days after his departure, both Rivers and his son received pardons.

Utrecht, a city in the Burundian Netherlands, offered the Duchess of York the opportunity to mourn. Margaret, just fourteen, wept often! Twelve-year-old George was uncharacteristically solemn. Both George and Richard returned to their books. Margaret studied along with them. When Cecily expressed surprise

64

that Margaret had learned to read, Margaret answered, "Someone had to help the boys!"

George chortled, "Wasn't that you who was asking me questions yesterday?"

"I only wanted to find out if you knew the answers."

George laughed out loud. "Answers about young maidens being rescued by daring knights would be more likely."

Cecily smiled ever so slightly, she lacked the heart to scold. The world was changing around her. Her daughters were presented with opportunities she had never had. Richard, seeing that his sister and mother were smiling, joined in the laughter as well. George rewarded him with a pat on the back. It was almost like old times. Almost!

From a sound sleep in the middle of the night, a noise awakened Richard. Startled, he looked about, but George was asleep. Suddenly, a sea of sorrow and a flood of tears overwhelmed Richard. When at last the pain in his heart eased, he was neither in a state of wakefulness nor sleep. It was as if he was between the world he considered real and some kind of dreamstate. He unexpectedly became aware of a recognizable hand upon his shoulder. George was snoring! Richard knew that his father was with him in the room.

Richard was never exactly certain what happened next. He felt his father's love for him. His own heart responded with an aching prayer for help. "God, in the name of Jesus, take my father's soul into Your Care!" Another, but distinctly different loving presence filled the room. The air around him somehow became substantive. A visible shift occurred. A flash of Light appeared. His father's soul was gone. George slept through the entire episode.

Richard knew with absolute certainty that his father's personality had survived death.

Unlike the specters that haunted Ludlow Castle, Richard, Duke of York, had found peace and moved on. It was nearly dawn before Richard was able to fall back asleep. He would tell no one, not even George!

The realm of Burgundy lay southeast of France and included rich farmlands and commercial cities — some of the wealthiest in all of Europe. When word of Edward's victory reached Duke Philip, he made elaborate preparations to have Cecily and her children escorted graciously to Bruges. The sixty-three year old Duke had the long, mis-shapened Valois nose. His kindly nature earned him the nickname, Philip the Good. After the royal family's arrival, he, himself, visited Cecily at the extravagantly prepared lodgings.

"Madam, I am most sorry to hear about the deaths of your husband, son and brother. Are you and the children all right?"

"Thank you, for your concern, Duke Philip. You are very kind. The accommodations you have arranged for us are quite lovely."

"Another day, perhaps, you and your children would enjoy seeing my library? But for tomorrow, there is a celebration in your honor.'

The red carpet was fully extended! A lavish tournament was followed by a sumptuous banquet, featuring performances by trained exotic beasts. Musical and theatrical pieces that had been inspired by sacred, secular and classic themes were also performed throughout the feast. Afterwards, Cecily enjoyed watching her sons' preoccupation with the performance of *Hercules.*

As Duke Philip promised, the following day he took them to visit his illustrious library. It was renowned throughout Europe for its fine collection of magnificently illuminated manuscripts bound in leather covers that were set with precious gems. He introduced them to his court historians. "Imagine that!" exclaimed Cecily, "Recording events as they transpire for future generations to call history."

"Better to be remembered in a good way!"

Before departing for England, the city of Burges gave the newly created English royal family a festive farewell banquet. The Duke lavished Cecily and Margaret with presents, including reams of finely woven clothe and silk. George and Richard were each given one of the classics, written in Latin and leather-bound. Included among the gifts were many bottles of fine Burgundy wine. "For King Edward's pleasure, my lady."

The Plantagenets were escorted by coach to Calais where they embarked for England. They had been summoned home to participate in the pomp and ritual of nineteen-year-old Edward's formal inauguration. All of the riches in Burgundy and even the performance of *Hercules* were ordinary in comparison to Edward. Edward meant for his brothers to share in his glory.

On Friday, June 26, ushered by city officials, Richard rode with Edward and George into London and on to London Tower. That evening, Richard and George, along with twenty-six other young noblemen, began the elaborate ritual of induction into the Knights of the Bath. Richard's rite began with a perfumed, luxurious bath, complete with singing. Verses from Ramon Lull's *Book on the Order of Chivalry* were read to him. He received instructions in the code of chivalry along with a stern warning not to break the code.

Later, Richard kept a knightly vigil in the Chapel of St. John. As he stood, he had a sense that most of knights were sleeping. William Hastings was more than likely with his brother, Edward, in the royal apartments at the Tower of

London. By tradition, a new king or queen resided at London Tower just prior to being crowned.

Sacraments of confession and mass took place at sunrise. Afterwards, Richard slept for only a few hours. Then he was dressed in fine knightly garb and led on horseback to the King. A knave preceding him carried Richard's spurs and sword. Edward IV commanded two knights to put Richard's spurs on him. The King dubbed Richard on the shoulders with his sword and kissed him. Smiling with wonderful satisfaction, Edward spoke, "Be thou a good knight!"

Richard and the other newly created Knights of the Bath each in turn walked to the high altar. The smell and smoke of pungent incense permeated the air. Wafting incense altered the light coming into the chapel through the stained glass windows. Richard imagined that in another time, the Knights of the Round Table would have gone through just such an induction. Richard listened intently, as each knight in turn swore allegiance. When it was his turn, Richard repeated the oath with conviction. "I swear to maintain the rights of the Church and offer my sword in her defense."

Leaving the chapel, the newly created Knights were greeted by the Master-Cook. "I, the King's Master-Cook, have come to receive your spurs as my fee. God forbid, if you do anything contrary to the Order of Knighthood, I shall hack your spurs from your heels."

With that, Richard and the others were escorted to a banquet. They were not the guests! They were the silent attendants, who stood guard as the older Knights of the Bath dined.

Richard's mind raced. It had been nearly two years since he had stood on the steps of the marker cross in Ludlow. He had forgotten how he had known what the Queen's captain looked like before he arrived. Now, for some unexpected reason, he remembered how he had seen the Queen's forces before their arrival in Ludlow. He was exhausted! He brought his mind sharply back to the banquet. "Discipline! Remain focused on the task at hand!" He found within him new surges of energy. "I must do my best so that Edward will be proud!"

On the afternoon of Sunday, June 28, 1461, Richard along with a gala retinue of knights, nobles and officials accompanied Edward to Westminster to witness his coronation. The commoners adored Edward. Multitudes had gathered to share in Edward's moment; everyone in the kingdom was on holiday. Edward responded to their cheers with passion and heart.

Warwick was among those few who focused their attention elsewhere. His aim was to read the faces, the attitudes of the peerage and others who mattered. It was at Westminster where Warwick noticed the unease of his Aunt Cecily.

Edward wasted little time in securing his family's estates and what was left of their fortune. He confirmed the York lands and titles to his mother. The Dowager Duchess of York, mother of the King, and a wealthy widow in her own right, fashioned herself the 'Queen by Right'. Dividing her time between her domains and court, Cecily continued her charities, supervised social and state functions at court and spent time with her children. Her self-appointed task of finding a suitable bride for Edward allowed her to dabble in foreign affairs. In the end, she favored a royal union with Isabella of Castile.

George was next in line to the throne. On Monday, Edward IV created him Duke of Clarence. William Hastings was made Lord Hastings and other faithful followers were awarded titles as well. Edward did not forget his youngest brother! On All Hallows Day, shortly after his ninth birthday,

Edward placed a cap of estate on Richard's head and created him Duke of Gloucester. In November, Richard and George were elected to fill two of the many vacant seats that the War of the Roses had created in the Knights of the Garter.

After long months of celebrations, George, Duke of Clarence, talked Edward into allowing him to remain at court. Edward insisted that George continue his studies. With the approval of his mother, Richard was to enter the household of the greatest lord in the realm, Richard Neville, Earl of Warwick.

Before leaving London, Richard had a welcomed opportunity to speak with Edward alone. He asked Edward about his generalship. Edward responded by telling Richard about the battle at Towton. When Edward was finished, Richard told Edward about his experience at the steps of the marker cross in the town of Ludlow two years before. Edward did not laugh! Richard asked, "Has anything like that happened to you?"

Edward hesitated, "I would not describe my experiences exactly the way you did. During a military campaign I do seem to somehow be able to know where my enemy is, how to approach the situation and where to best position my men." Edward paused to size up his young listener. "It has happened on a few occasions during a battle, when it seems that everyone and everything has slowed down. In that moment, I know what will happen next." Edward had never told anyone before, not even William Hastings. "We will keep this matter to ourselves."

Richard was elated that his brother, the King, would confide in him. He took in a deep breath that filled his chest. His eyes filled with admiration for Edward. "I am your trusted liegeman!"

Edward knew his brother spoke from his heart. He grasped Richard's shoulders with his large hands. "We will speak again!"

The Great House of Neville

Richard had been both relieved to hear that he was not an anomaly and disappointed that his brother was unable to offer him further assistance or understanding. Edward knew instinctively that while their words differed, Richard, like himself, had inherited Edward I's propensity for skilled generalship. Edward possessed the uncanny ability to remember conversations, but this particular discussion remained in the forefront of his memory. While George's attributes were those of an ambassador of good will, Richard's skills might one day serve him in the field.

A royal guard accompanied Richard Plantagenet, second in line to the throne of England, on the five-day journey to Middleham Castle, located in the North Riding of Yorkshire. Wherever the party stopped to rest for the night, Richard was welcomed with formal protocol. He heard repeated over and over again, similar comments, "Richard looks like his father, not his brother, King Edward!" For the first time in his life, Richard was not only traveling without George, but he was being contrasted with someone other than George.

The red highlights in Richard's hair, his blue eyes, straight nose and high cheekbones were characteristic of the Plantagenets. The line of his jaw mirrored his determinism. A good-looking boy, he stood average in height.

Traditionally, a young prince completed his conventional schooling in the household of an esteemed courtier. Formal studies and practical experiences helped to mold a boy's character. Richard was no exception; he would learn firsthand the finesse of politics and the qualities necessary for estate management. He would observe the qualities of good lordship — how to protect and defend the best interests of servants. Loyal servants support and protect their masters!

Richard was to live with Richard Neville, the Earl of Warwick. Warwick was the obvious choice and it was an honor for Warwick to be asked. Warwick and Edward determined beforehand that Richard would be treated exactly like the other young boys assigned to Warwick's household, in the same manner that the Duke of York had insisted that Edward and Edmund be treated at Ludlow Castle.

The Nevilles were hereditary lords of Raby and Brancepath in County Durham. Richard Neville's grandfather, Ralph, had married Joan Beaufort. Thus, the Earl of Warwick traced his bloodline back to John of Gaunt. The Duke of York had grown up in Ralph Neville's household, where he had fallen in love with Ralph Neville's youngest daughter, Cecily. Thus, Richard Neville and Prince Richard were cousins. Richard Neville's father married Alice, the daughter of the Earl of Salisbury. After the Earl of Salisbury was captured and executed at Wakefield, his title and domains passed onto Alice. When Richard Neville married Anne Beauchamp, he inherited the title, Earl of Warwick, and the vast estates accompanying that right of peerage.

Warwick's disposition was easily displeased. Overreacted to adversity, his ego was vulnerable. He was controlling and determined to succeed. Warwick identified himself with his property and possessions, but it was prestige he craved as much as power. By managing the young King's affairs he had the authority and popularity he desired.

There was no middle ground or gray area — in Warwick's world everything and everybody was right or wrong, good or evil. It was either his way or the Roman roadway. While he was a Lancaster by blood, it served Warwick's best interests to back his Aunt Cecily's husband, their children and the Yorkist cause. Though Edward's superior generalship abilities surpassed those of Warwick and other generals in the kingdom, without Warwick the Yorkist cause would never have made it off the ground.

Middleham Castle touted one of the largest keeps in all of England; it was Warwick's favorite! Richard's party approached the castle from the north, passing through the small town of Middleham. Arriving at the small tower, which guarded the outer end of the drawbridge and the gatehouse itself, they were greeted by the Captain of the Guard. Richard sized up the castle in his mind. The gatehouse turrets were raised an extra stage at the corners and projected diagonally outwards from the face of the wall. Battlements on the remaining walls extended outwards and were supported by projecting stones. The openings created by this particular architecture afforded soldiers an advantage point from which to shoot down on would be invaders. Figures of knights carved in stone were fixed to the battlements.
Once within the inner bailey walls, Richard was escorted to the oblong keep, the walls of which measured 10 to 12 feet thick. A defensible stone staircase led to the covered first floor entrance. The enormous edifice measured 8,190 square feet. Situated on the west half of the first floor was the Great Chamber as well as the Inner Chamber — rooms designed for the lord of Middleham's personal use. Located on the east half of the first floor was the Great Hall, where those seeking an audience with the lord of Middleham were escorted. Disputes were settled in the Great Hall. It also served as the site for extravagant feasts and opulent parties. Huge tapestries hung on the white plastered walls. Three round-headed windows in the north wall

provided most of the interior light. A spiral staircase in the southeast corner led down to the ground floor. Located on the ground floor were the dark cellar and the kitchen with its high, small square windows, which provided minimal lighting.

The same spiral staircase ascended upwards to the viewing platform, which was on the same level as the battlements. Warwick escorted Richard to the top. Immediately to the southwest stood the ruins of a Norman mote-and-bailey fortress. To the south, like the castle itself, the vast wide scope of the rolling moors stretched upwards to meet the heavens. Looking northwards past the village, at the bottom of a steep slope, ran the River Ure. Encompassing the entire castle lay the breathtakingly beautiful Wensleydale countryside. Beyond farmer's fields lay dense forests through which well-traveled roads led to bustling abbeys, stone castles and tiny villages.

The people of the North were conservative by nature, slow to change loyalties and deeply religious. They held as firmly to their persuasions, as they did to the land; quick to defend both! The Nevilles had been their good and generous lords.

Francis Lovell and Robert Percy, like Richard, were also attached to Warwick's household. The boys celebrated holidays in the North with Warwick, his wife and their two delicate daughters. Isabel was Richard's age and Anne was four years younger. Sometimes, the boys rode into York, the metropolis of the North. They stayed the night at one of the religious houses. On occasion, they might ride with Warwick to Nappa Hall, where they listened to James Metcalfe tell battle stories. Visiting Lord Scrope at Bolton Castle was another frequent destination. He, too, had interesting stories to tell!

Richard Plantagenet, Francis Lovell, Robert Percy and the other apprentices studying knightly conduct were called henchmen. They were assigned to the care of the Master of the Henchmen, who was responsible for all aspects of their learning and training. He was a burly, tall man with large features and an even larger head. Bushy red eyebrows stood out against his blue-green eyes and ruddy complexion. Tufts of shaggy red hair projected straight outwards, something like a sheep dog, and his hair was often in disarray. When he removed his helmet, sweat clamped a ring of hair in a circle around his head and unruly clumps of red hair shot out in a variety of directions. All in all, his outward appearance belied the poetry residing in his heart. He was a lord as well as a knight for only nobility were allow to handle the Earl's horses. His French was impeccable. He had spent many years campaigning against Charles VII and possessed a natural affinity for languages. It was in France where he had received his scars; the old wound across his left cheek was from a dagger. However, it was the lance wound in his right thigh that put an end to his military career. The henchmen called him "Master".

The henchmen rose at dawn, heard mass and then ate breakfast in the bustle of the Great Hall. The meal consisted of meat, bread and ale. The Master of the Henchmen sat at the head of their table, taking careful note of his charge's manners. Proper table manners and etiquette were part and parcel of the henchmen's training. After breakfast, the boys put on their harness and assembled in the tiltyard to practice with swords, battle-axes and other weapons. The boys learned Latin, French, law, mathematics and music, including how to play an instrument, dance and sing. Like Edward, Richard easily grasped data and concepts.

The henchmen studied Christian doctrines, the art of war, the rules of knighthood and courtly behavior. They would learn to hunt with hounds, falcons or hawks. Birds of prey were considered valuable. Manuals, such as the *Treatise of Falconry* by the Emperor Frederick II of Germany, gave detailed instructions on how to care for and train birds of prey. But first, the henchmen concentrated on riding skills.

The Master of the Henchmen's expertise with horses and knowledge of horsemanship was recognized throughout the Midlands. He taught riding skills simply and without cynicism. His instructions put into words and practice ideals that the Duke of York had taught his sons. "Now, boys, there will be people who tell you that these beasts have no soul. To them, I would say, loyalty is a condition of the faithful heart. It is that, which the soul strives for. As these so-called beasts are capable of such allegiances, how can they not have a soul?"
The following day on the moors, the Master of the Henchmen lined the henchmen up facing him. "Your horses are capable of moving in other directions besides forwards. Someday, asking your horse to go backwards may save your life." The Master of the Henchmen demonstrated by gently playing with the reins to set his horse's head so that his neck broke at the pole and the horse's head was vertical to the ground. "Now, I pull up gently but firmly by moving my shoulders back and press on the horse's sides with the calves of my legs." His horse immediately dropped his hindquarters and with his neck arched, he took large steps backwards. "To make him go forward, I relax my shoulders and keep pressing with my calves." His horse stopped moving backwards and walked forwards. "As soon as he moves forwards, I stop pressing with my calves. My legs rest against the horse's sides. Now, try it!"
The henchmen followed the Master of the Henchmen's instructions. Lovell's horse popped his head high into the air. "It's all right,

Lovell! Just keep asking him to go backwards until he arches his neck down and gives to you. When he gives, it is more comfortable him. By asking until he gives, you are helping him to figure that out." Lovell's horse arched his neck, dropped his haunches and took a large step behind. "Good! He has given to you. Now, keep asking him to go straight backwards a few more steps. Good! Tell him he's a good boy and ask him to go forward. Don't give your reins away when you ask him to go ahead! Keep a slight feel on his mouth and move your shoulders forward." Lovell's horse moved ahead. "Good! You are teaching him."

Richard wanted to please his master, but his horse was not moving. He applied his spurs. The Master of the Henchmen intervened firmly, "If you use your spurs in a situation like this, what kind of effort are you going to have to use when you need a big response?" The Master of the Henchmen looked around at the henchmen. "Keep lifting the reins firmly towards your shoulders by moving your shoulders back. At the same time, press with your legs. If your horse is not responding, know that he will eventually give in to you."

Richard tried again. After a short while, his horse shot his head in the air and moved backwards. "Master, his head is up!"

"Keep asking!" After more than two-dozen steps, Richard's horse settled down and took a relaxed step backwards. "Good! Keep asking! After he takes a couple of steps like that, relax your shoulders and bring your hands down into riding position." Richard's horse stepped forward. The Master of the Henchmen gave encouragement, "Good! Now stop pressing with your calves. Allow your legs relax on your horse's sides."

The Master of the Henchmen patted his horse and demonstrated backing up again. This time, he did not move his hands up towards his shoulders, he simply moved his shoulders back. "Your goal is to use light cues to initiate a response." His steed immediately responded by arching his neck, dropping his hindquarters and taking large strides backwards. "It'll take a few months for your horse to become as adept as old Darby here. We'll keep working on it. Just be patient with yourselves and your mounts!"

The Master of the Henchmen turned his attention back to the group. "Percy, you're sitting on that horse as if you were sitting in a chair. Look, at your knees! They are up! All of you, adjust your seat so that you are sitting in the front of your saddle with your seat bones planted on the saddle." Francis Lovell tilted his hips forward. "Good! Now keep your weight solidly in your feet and keep your seat bones in contact with the saddle. The man who stays on his horse during a battle is the one who has his weight in his feet and his seat in the saddle!" Richard checked his seat, watching his fellow henchmen eagerly adjusting their seats.

"If you want to go forward, press your calves against the side of your horse. Good! Now, push him into the bridle. When he gives, relax your arms and reward him, but keep a slight contact. Now let your seat move with the horse. Percy, let the horse move you. Good! Let's see you back your horse up once again!"

Richard's mount was a gift from Edward. The steed was astonishingly handsome, as well as unusually spirited for a draft horse. Draft horses were strong enough to carry a knight in full armor but they could be obstinate. From the time the Welsh horse had arrived at Middleham, Richard wondered if the horse wasn't going to be too much for him. He never said anything. Richard was determined to ride the horse.

Now, he was having difficult and doubted his abilities. His horse was waving his head in the air, with as much grace and style as a laundress shaking out a shirt. Richard pulled back hard with both reins. The horse responded by laying into the bit, opening his mouth and gnarling his head around with even more determination. "You'll not be winning a tug of war with that horse, Gloucester. When he sticks his head up in the air, gently squeeze on one rein and then the other, until he gives to you. If you use your reins, you must follow up with your legs. So, immediately after you squeeze and release with one rein, press with your calves and release. Keep going! Keep your reins up!" Richard's horse at last arched his neck, lowered his haunches and stepped back boldly. "Well done! Now reward him by relaxing your reins a bit and allow him to go forwards." Richard gave his horse the reins. "You're throwing the horse away! Keep a contact on the reins." Richard picked up his reins.

The Master of the Henchmen rode a ways in front of the oncoming line of henchmen. He brought his horse to a halt so that the boys were able to see what he was doing. "If you want to stop, take your legs off your horse, drop your heels and seat, move your legs forward slightly. Lift the reins towards your shoulders as if you were going to back up. As your horse takes his last step, squeeze with your calves and you will move him from behind and into the bridle. As soon as he stops, relax your legs and your shoulders. Any questions?"

Percy broke the silence. "Master, I thought we were supposed to keep our heels down all of the time. How is stopping going to be different?"

"When you ride, you do not lock your heels rigidly down!"

Richard's horse wasn't stopping. He pulled on his horse. The horse again responded by bracing himself on the bit and Richard's arms. Patiently, the Master of the Henchmen went over his instructions again. "Gloucester, the quieter you are with this horse the better off you are going to be! Ask him to walk forward again!" Richard asked and the horse responded immediately.

"This time, instead of trying to bring him to a halt with both reins at the same time, try squeezing one rein and then the other. See how gently you can bring this animal to a halt. Take your legs off of him for a moment. Now, drop your heels, push your legs forward a bit and sit down into the horse. Bring your shoulders back and then press him into a halt." It worked!

"We are now going to do the same thing at a trot. Weight in your stirrups. Keep your seat bones in contact with the saddle — this is your foundation! Press your horse into a walk with your legs. Good! Let your seat follow your horse! Gently tweak your right rein with your ring finger and then do the same with your left rein and your ring finger. In this way, you set your horse up. Now press him into the trot with your calves."

The boys took off at a trot. "Lovell, once your steed is trotting, stop pressing your knees into him! Keep your legs gently on his sides and your weight in your feet!" Francis didn't even know he had been pressing with his legs. He relaxed his legs and found that he had been clutching his horse. "Good! Bring your shoulders back!" The horse slowed down.

"Percy, stop balancing on the reins! Keep your weight in your feet and shift your weight from side to side with the movement of the horse. Don't stiffen your back! Relax your body!" Henry began bouncing on his horse. "If you lose your seat, bring your horse back to a walk and recommence."

Richard's horse began gathering speed, laid into the bit and lost his balance. As a result, the horse stopped pushing himself forwards with his rear legs and was falling forwards onto his front legs. "He's not slowing down!"

"Slow him down the same way that you brought him to a halt! Take your legs away from his sides and when you put them back on, bring your shoulders back! If he's not listening, pull back evenly, not harshly, with first your right rein and then your left. At the same time, press your seat straight down into the saddle and push your legs slightly ahead!" The Master of the Henchmen called out, "Your ankles are stiff! Keep them down! Keep them loose!" Richard's horse responded. "Good! Relax your shoulders when he has slowed down to the speed you want."

Richard's horse responded. The Master of the Henchmen rode up next to him and halted. "Let me show you another way to slow him down or bring him to a halt. You will have more confidence if you have more control over your horse." Richard was eager for anything that would help.

"If your horse is not listening to you, pull both reins back evenly and gently towards either your right or your left shoulder." The Master of the Henchmen demonstrated so that all of the henchmen could observe. He squeezed his horse forward with his legs. After several steps, he brought both of his shoulders back but both his right and left hands were slightly to the left. "Keep the reins parallel to one another! Notice that the horse's head is bent ever so slightly at the pole to the right. When he is bent like this he cannot lay into the bit. You will be able to bring him to a halt if he is not listening." The Master of the Henchmen looked intently at his charges. "Be patient with your steeds and yourselves! You are both in training!"

It was a lot to manage and remember all at once. Though he had to concentrate intently, he was beginning to enjoy his horse. He smiled! He was going to make it! Edward would be pleased! The Master of the Henchmen's voice broke Richard's focus. "Gloucester, thumbs up! If you ride with dog's paws you hunch over and lose effectiveness of the give and take in your shoulders!"

Duly diligent, Richard struggled with the complexity of moving one leg one way, maneuvering the other leg differently, and at the same time, encountering a similar struggle with his arms and hands. Richard, like the other boys, admired the Master of the Henchmen. The boys understood too well how untypical and unusual their teacher was. Indeed, they were lucky. Richard thanked God with his whole heart for the opportunities that his station afforded him. He sighed and his horse snorted loudly. "Pat him, Gloucester! He's relaxed! He's learning to trust you!"

Richard's arms and legs remained slender. However, he was strong for his size. His agility allowed him to hold his own in physical activities. He took chivalry to heart, and was part and parcel of the growing comradery amongst the henchmen. Like the other boys, Richard and Francis were exhausted by bedtime, but they still managed to find a last bit of vigor with which to share stories, hopes, fears and secrets.

One of the secrets Richard shared with Francis was the time when he, along with his mother and brother, had stood on the steps of the marker cross in the town of Ludlow before dawn. Francis listened attentively! Richard asked, "What do you make of it, Francis?"

"Maybe this ability is what allows a general to move his men into an advantageous position at the right time. They call it savvy or fortune!"

Richard's conversation with Edward came to mind. As much as he would have valued Francis' opinion, Richard kept Edward's confidence. Instead he said, "According to you, it was not providence that shone on Henry V, but his ability to perceive beyond what he saw."

"Time and chance enter into all things. Say, Warwick is taking us to Lord Metcalfe's tomorrow."

"No doubt, he will recount stories of his military campaigns with Henry V."

Francis Lovell was extremely intelligent, down-to-earth and two years older than Richard. He was exceedingly grateful to the King for his patronage; Edward paid Warwick £1000 to raise both Richard and Francis. Francis was even more appreciative to find that the King's brother was not full of himself. Robert Percy was their companion and friend, as were Metcalfe's sons, but it was Richard and Francis who had hit it off from the start. It was the best time of their lives!

In February 1462, George, Duke of Clarence, was appointed Lieutenant of Ireland, the post his father held when he was named heir apparent to the throne. Clarence's deputy administered the office. This was not enough for George; he went back to his brother to ask for his own property and manors. Edward refused! George's charms were unable to persuade the King to change his mind. George pondered as to whether or not to play his trump card. In August, George set aside both his concerns and his scruples. He spoke to Edward in private. Edward was stunned as he listened to George state, "Your father is not my father. He was a commoner and an archer!

"You speak treason to your own brother?"

"I am only repeating what I heard from our mother."

Edward was aghast. He sought out his mother. The Duchess apologized, "I never meant you harm. However, it is true."

Edward was horrified! His kingship was at stake. If he stepped down George would assume the throne. George would be over his head! England would become as unstable as a fool teetering on a mote wall. Unable to find another option, Edward rationalized. Through his mother's bloodlines his lineage traced back directly to the old kings of England. In the end, Edward granted George the lands and manors, which had been forfeited by the Earl of Northumberland. However, Edward was perturbed. He looked for a way to show George his displeasure. Less than two weeks later, lands and manors forfeited by the Earl of Oxford were granted to Richard, Duke of Gloucester. In addition, Richard was given the lordships of Richmond and Pembroke. Edward sat back to see what George would do.

Edward did not have to wait long! In a fit of anger, George sought a private audience. Reproachfully, George rebuffed the King. "I swear I will tell every man, woman and child in the kingdom that you're an archer's son. How can you bestow more property on Richard than you do on me, England's rightful king?"

Edward had an answer prepared. "I will transfer the lordship of Richmond to you. George, this is the end of it! Swear to me this is so!"

"I swear on our father's grave!"

"Approach me again on this matter and you will be spending your days looking over your shoulder." Edward looked for another way to show George his displeasure. He made Richard Admiral of England, Ireland and Aquitaine.

In London, Edward IV strove to win the support of the Lancastrians by means of royal pardons and diplomacy. In the North, Warwick and his brother, John Neville, Lord Montagu, worked to subdue uprisings. Along the coasts and in the Marches of Wales and Scotland, Queen Margaret and those allied to her continued to instigate turmoil and trouble. Three times the Lancastrians invaded Northumberland. Three times the Nevilles trounced the Lancastrians, who endured heavy losses.

Bamburgh, Dunstanburgh and Alnwick castles, however, remained in Lancastrian hands. With Henry VI safely in Scotland, Queen Margaret sailed to France in the summer of 1462, to secure the help of Louis XI. On October 25, under the command of Piers de Breze, Queen Margaret and her forces invaded Northumberland. When she heard that both Warwick and Edward had assembled armies and were marching against her, she had second thoughts. She retreated to her ships, which were subsequently shattered in a ferocious storm at sea. Margaret's off again/on again luck was on again. She and Piers de Breze were among the few who were not drowned or captured.

King Edward came down with a sudden and severe case of measles. It was left up to Warwick and Montagu to retake the three imposing Northumberland fortresses. When he recovered the King stopped in York on his way back to London to celebrate Christmas. Edward sent a contingent of his personal guard to Middleham to escort Richard to his quarters.

Richard accompanied Edward on state matters. He listened enthusiastically to Edward's plans and strategies for bringing peace to a troubled realm. At dinner, Edward listened to Richard's rendition of Warwick's last battle. Using cutlery and plate, Richard reenacted the confrontation. Occasionally, Edward interrupted asking, "Why do you think Warwick did that?" Or "Was there another way to approach the castle?" With each of Richard's answers, Edward took note with the critical ear of a university dean. William Hastings smiled knowingly, as Richard converted a knife into Warwick's left flank, which took up position to attack a makeshift castle - a roasted shank of lamb. Richard Neville, Earl of Warwick had fully accomplished Edward's goal! The young prince emerged from his tutorage strong, capable and knowledgeable. Richard's keen penchant for grasping the complexities and dynamics of war, along with his training, would make him invaluable in the field. Indeed, Edward was proud!

Early in January 1463, the three castles were under Warwick's control. Shortly thereafter, Edward was strong enough to travel. With Richard at his side, the brothers rode to Fotheringhay to perform the sacred filial duty of honoring their father's death. The ceremony rivaled that of Edward's coronation.

Not to be outdone, two weeks later, the prestigious Neville brothers - George, Bishop of Exeter and Chancellor, Lord Montagu and the Earl of Warwick - escorted the remains of their father and brother to Bisham Abbey in Buckinghamshire. Along with the recently diseased Countess of Salisbury, the remains of the Neville lords were laid to rest amidst magnificence. Lord Hastings and the Duke of Clarence represented the King. For the first time in his life, George was left without words to adequately describe the splendor.

Edward returned to London with Richard in late February. While at court, Richard attended sessions of Parliament. Many of the faces he recognized from Edward's coronation; others were from the North. His eleven-year-old mind listened attentively. As petitions and requests were being acted upon, Richard reflected at how proud his father would be to see Edward IV fulfilling his dreams of good government and equal justice. At the end of spring, Richard returned to Middleham Castle. The Marches of Scotland were in a flurry. Uprisings were seemingly everywhere!

The Scots and Lancastrians retook Bamburgh, Dunstanburgh and Alnwick castles. Warwick immediately marched north with Richard in attendance in the rear. While Warwick recaptured the fortresses, Lord Montagu laid siege to Norham Castle, sending the Scottish forces back to Scotland. Queen Margaret and her son retreated to France. Weary of dying for the Lancastrian cause, the Scots signed a ten-month truce with Edward IV.

In London, Edward IV courted Lancastrians to accept his government. In particular, by flattery and conciliation, he wooed the support of Henry

Beaufort, Duke of Somerset. Hoping to show the populace that he ruled by popular consent, as opposed to force, in the fall of 1463, Edward departed for York with Somerset and 200 of Somerset's men. Citizens of Northampton were appalled to see the King in the hands of York's oldest enemy. The men of Northampton took up arms, rising against Somerset. They would have killed Somerset had Edward not intervened.

With the unrelenting persistence of a fly, Queen Margaret unerringly returned to Wales for support in January 1464. At the same time, in spite of his oath to the contrary, Somerset busily organized a desperate Lancastrian effort from Bamburgh Castle to reclaim the crown. It took two months before Edward and Warwick were able to bring peace to the Midlands and return to London.

Edward and Warwick together worked out a plan to permanently rid Northumberland of Lancastrian forces. Edward snatched whatever funds he could lay hold of. He then dispatched commissions of array for all twenty-two counties in southern England. Richard, Duke of Gloucester, not yet twelve years old, was made sole commissioner for nine of the counties. George, Duke of Clarence, did not receive a single commission.

On April 25, 1464, John Neville, the Lord Montagu, routed Somerset's superior forces at Hedgeley Moor. Ralph Percy, the Earl of Northumberland, who had been pardoned and sworn allegiance to Edward IV, was among the Lancastrians who lay slain on the battlefield. On May 15, Montagu battered what was left of the Lancastrians at Hexham. Somerset and more than two dozen leading Lancastrians were captured, tried and beheaded. The Crown seized Percy's title and lands. On May 27th, Edward rewarded John Neville with the earldom of Northumberland. The new Earl of Northumberland was exceptionally proud and immeasurably grateful!

Other players in the drama retreated, waiting for an opportunity to play out their respective roles. Queen Margaret was forced home to her father. Somerset's younger brother and the Duke of Exeter were given sanctuary in Burgundy, where the Duke lent his support to the Lancastrian cause by banning the import of English cloth. Richard returned to Middleham to continue his training and studies.

Traditionally, a king's council gave the final approval over a prospective marriage. Edward had a partiality for older, beautiful women. He defied custom by entering into a secret marriage contract with a stunningly attractive older woman, the widow, Lady Eleanor Butler. She was the daughter of the old Talbot, the Earl of Shrewsbury. Edward had met lovely Lady Eleanor when she came to him to plead her cause. She asked Edward to restore her lands to her. Edward saw to it that two manors were entitled to Lady Eleanor. Afterwards, he emboldened himself upon her, but she would not yield to his sexual advances. Edward then had Stillington, Bishop of Bath and Wells, marry them secretly. He would wait for the appropriate time to tell Warwick and the rest of the Council.

Edward, however, had not entirely forgotten Elizabeth Woodville! On May 1, Edward was on his way to Leicester and thoughts of Elizabeth played upon his mind. He offered a feeble pretext to his men and departed alone to see Elizabeth, who still refused to succumb to his adulations! That same day, for better or worse, Edward married Elizabeth. The only witness to the nuptials was Elizabeth's mother, a woman so arduous and conniving that many considered her to be a witch.

Bubble, Bubble Toil and Trouble!

England had two masters. So long as they were both in accord, peace prevailed. Edward had been willing and eager for Warwick's advice. However, increasing, Warwick simply acted without conferring with Edward. Diplomats and kings alike were uncertain as to which king had the last word. Warwick's correspondence with Louis of France made the answer quite clear. He wrote, "There are two kings in England —'M. de Warwick and another, whose name thoroughly escapes me."

On the Continent Warwick worked diligently to repair French/English relationships. He determined it would serve England for Edward to marry Lois XI's sister-in-law, Bona of Savoy. England's other master, Edward IV, was distrustful of Louis XI, and was busy cementing relationships with England's traditional ally, Burgundy. Matters came to a head when on September 15, 1464, Warwick blatantly urged Edward to formally sign the French marriage contract. Backed into a corner, Edward replied that he was already married to Elizabeth Woodville. The news astounded the Earl of Warwick and the remainder of the Council!

Warwick was furious! Deeming his dissatisfaction justifiable, he rightly considered that the King's marriage should have been politically motivated for England's best interests. Edward's marriage to a French princess would have put an end to Queen Margaret's hopes of seeing her son on the English throne. The Lancastrian cause would have been snuffed out once and for all. However, it would have also given France the license to absorb and incorporate the wealthy ducal fiefs of Brittany and Burgundy. It was a sacrifice Warwick was willing to make. After all, he reasoned, a king granted fiefs to a lord for his lifetime only. Upon the lord's death, these estates were returned to the crown.

Bitterly, the King and Earl argued loudly in public. Warwick's deprecating remarks traveled on the unsteady wings of gossip throughout the kingdom. Unexpectedly, there came a welcomed calm. To outward appearances, the amiable relationship between Warwick and Edward returned to normal. Warwick acquiesced! He could generously forgive one rash transgression, thoughtless though it was. Warwick resumed negotiations with Louis XI. He had another Plantagenet to bargain with — Edward's beautiful sister, Princess Margaret.

By marrying Elizabeth Woodville, Edward had asserted his independence from Warwick. However, Edward also wished harmony between himself and Warwick, his kin and friend. The Nevilles were a prop to his throne. To manage the task of restoring an accord, Edward relied on his charm and generosity. He asked Warwick and the Duke of Clarence to escort his wife, Elizabeth, into Reading Abbey where the entire court honored her as Queen. Soon afterwards, George Neville, Bishop of Exeter and Chancellor of England, was elevated to Archbishop of York. Edward's marriage to Elizabeth Woodville was a setback for Warwick, but only a setback.

Warwick was not alone in his personal dislike of Queen Elizabeth in particular, and the Woodvilles in general. Gossip had it that Elizabeth Woodville put a spell on the King. Warwick was not superstitious; he believed in neither ghosts nor enchantments. He did, however, seriously question Edward's sanity in marrying the woman. The Council was put out! Cecily was outraged that her son had not only married beneath his station, but to a woman whom she considered outlandishly vane and juvenile.

George was first in line to the throne but second to Edward in many matters. While George was tall, Edward was taller. George was strong; Edward was stronger. George was handsome; Edward was handsomer! George was smart; Edward was smarter. George was a good commander, brave and able in combat; Edward's generalship abilities were unparalleled and he fought like a Titan. How could one win? The thought that kept George afloat was his mother's revelation, which offered a reversal of fortune and family positioning. Her statement had been so astounding that George had made her repeat it. "Edward is not the son of the Duke of York!"

After Edward announced his marriage to Elizabeth Woodville, Cecily told several people about her indiscretion. She even submitted to examination. George hoped, even daydreamed that the English populace would be aghast at the Duchess' disclosure, and denounce Edward. He would then be called upon him to sit upon the Coronation Throne. Surely, the Speaking Stone would sing out its approval. It didn't happen! Edward was too loved! Those who heard dismissed it as gossip!

Cecily did not notice immediately the change that came over George. It crept up on her! One day, it came to her attention that George's jokes often took on a cynical tone. He seemed to mull matters over, as if he were masticating a tough steak. When she asked him what the problem was, he answered emphatically, "I should be king of England!" Cecily made a mental note not to tell Richard.

Ireland enjoyed peace. The island faired under the evenhanded justice administered by the Plantagenets. In addition, the Irish had fond memories of the old Duke of York and his family.

When the Deputy Lieutenant of Ireland, the Earl of Desmond, arrived in London to clear accusations against him, he sought an audience with Edward IV. They were old childhood friends and shared many interests. It was when they were out hunting one day that Edward asked Desmond, "What do you think of my marriage?"

"Your Queen is gorgeous and virtuous, but had you married a foreign princess you would have been guaranteed a foreign alliance."

Edward accepted Desmond's frank answer as an observation, hardly an attack upon his new wife. When the exonerated Desmond left for Ireland, Edward gave him gifts for his service to the Crown. Not long afterwards, Edward told Elizabeth what Desmond had said. He guilelessly assumed that she would be pleased that Desmond considered her beautiful and righteous. Edward did not yet know Elizabeth.

The Queen responded with vehemence not often seen on the battlefield! Her reaction surprised Edward, as he had not seen this side of his attractive wife's character. He made excuses, rationalizing her behavior. Perhaps, it could be attributed to a bit of undigested poultry? Or maybe it was her time of the month? Nonetheless, Edward made a mental note, "Never shall I speak of such matters to my wife."

Edward had his own plans for the re-conquest of France; his subjects expected him to reclaim the territory lost by Henry VI. Edward kept his ambitions secret, as they ran completely contrary to Warwick's political efforts. The King was not yet ready to play out his hand. One of the problems Edward faced was that the Nevilles were in complete control of northern England. Edward was not quite sure how to bring the North into the fold. Foreseeing that he would come up against Warwick again, Edward recalled Richard to court in the spring of 1465. If the situation escalated, he wanted the Richard on his side.

Richard had just completed the most disciplined coarse in martial arts, chivalry and academics offered in all of England. He was by nature straight-laced and devotedly religious. On the other hand, he also liked wearing fine garments, though he was not nearly the clotheshorse Edward was.

Most of the peers resided in family castles or townhouses while they were at court in London. Richard resided at Baynard's Castle with the Duchess of York, who divided her time between her northern estates and London. Such castles and townhouses were situated along the Thames River, allowing lords and ladies to travel by barge to Westminster Palace or Windsor.

The river was the preferred method of travel. London's muddy streets were potholed. Crowded with travelers, pedestrians, carriages, men on horseback and stray dogs, an honest man had to be watchful of pickpockets. In addition, there was always the eminent danger of being drenched in household sewage thrown out a window. London Bridge was the only bridge across the River Thames, connecting one side of London with the other. The ferrymen intended to keep it that way.

London was a leading city. Her citizens were considered well off by European standards. Within her walls just about anything anyone would want could be found. In the heart of London, St. Paul's Gothic 450-foot spire dominated the city's skyline. Inns were typically filled with pilgrims on their way to Canterbury, or another cathedral or abbey where the bones of saints or relics resided. A pilgrim's journey was a penance in reparation for sins. Arriving at their destination, they surrendered to the mercy of God, pleading for intervention through the benevolence of a particular saint. Professional pilgrims were paid by the wealthy to make the pilgrimage and pray on their behalf.

England's commerce passed through London's docks, bringing merchants and sailors from the Continent and beyond. Actors, who performed at the Globe and Rose theatres, gathered in the taverns along with London's other visitors and citizens. Attorneys were available for hire at The Old Hall of Lincoln's Inn. On the eastern edge of the city, The Tower of London, a fortified palace, was the starting point for the wall that encircled the city. Lambeth Palace, the London residence of the Archbishop of Canterbury, stood across the river from the Palace of Westminster.

Edward III had made significant improvements to Westminster Palace. Tersely divided, the government operated from the Greater Palace, while the Privy Palace served as the royal residence. The King's Bathroom featured running hot and cold water. Edward constructed a belfry along the south wall of Westminster Hall, housing a bell weighing 9,261 pounds. St. Stephen's Chapel was completed in magnificent splendor. The vaulted timbered ceiling and walls were stenciled in gold. Golden statues flanked the marble altar. Eight panels beneath the windows commemorated Christian events. The niches between the windows were ornately carved. The windows were stained glass, allowing colored lights to illuminate the inner opulence.

The King and his court frequently changed residence, to allow the palace to be cleaned and aired. To accommodate everyone, Edward III reconstructed and fortified Windsor Castle. Windsor was the seat for The Order of the Garter and the priestly College of St. George. In the Round Tower Edward installed a mechanical weight-driven clock. Royal apartments were constructed around two lavish courtyards. The apartments were built of stone and splendidly adorned with stone-ribbed ceilings supported on slender Octagonal piers. The furniture was elaborately carved wood. Velvet cushions were placed on the chairs. Beautiful tapestries hung on the wall for decoration; in the winter they helped to keep the warmth from the large fireplaces in each room.

When Edward IV moved to his lesser households, his full staff did not accompany him. These residences included manors in the Thames Valley and Henry III's hunting lodge in Windsor Great Park. More often than not, the Queen did not accompany the King on these excursions.

Not long after his arrival in London, Edward introduced Richard to his Queen. Elizabeth welcomed Richard, though not genially. Richard was too young to notice the chill. He assumed it was her nature. Edward's brothers, like William Hastings, took Edward's time away from the Queen and her family! George, who made a point of being present for the introductions, observed Elizabeth's distain. He laughed to himself, "Obviously the woman does not show any favoritism to my younger brother! Elizabeth is equally jealous of the both of us."

Queen Elizabeth was not the only difficulty. Woodvilles were everywhere. They seemingly tripped over one another in a mad dash to climb the rungs of the social ladder, which endeared them to no one. The old nobility resented the highhanded treatment meted out to them by the Woodvilles. In particular they grumbled amongst themselves about compulsory marriages forced upon members of their peerage!

Elizabeth's sisters had been married off to the most eligible bachelors in the realm. Those who had succumbed to Woodville ambitions included Lord Herbert's son and heir, the Earl of Arundel's heir, the son of the Earl of Essex, the Earl of Kent's heir and the 12-year old Duke of Buckingham. Elizabeth had two sons from her previous marriage. She paid a considerable sum so that her eldest son, Thomas Grey, could marry the Duke of Exeter's heiress, who had been promised to Warwick's nephew. However, the match that aroused the most notoriety was that of Elizabeth's brother, John Woodville.

Richard had been somewhat prepared. Before leaving Middleham, he and his friends had read the report by a chronicler. "Catherine, Dowager Duchess of Norfolk, a mere slip of a girl about 80 years old, was married to John Woodville, the Queen's brother, aged 20 years." Lords, gentry and commoners alike resented the Queen and her family. One overly bearing, highly motivated queen had just been forced to leave the country. Now England was being presented with yet another!

Courtiers and ladies-in-waiting wore the latest fashions, wiling away their time amidst freshly cut flowers and music that played in every room. Holy days and feast days of saints offered a change in venue, opportunities for pageants, games of skill and banquets. Anthony Woodville, Lord Scales, was England's most skilled jouster, as well as an accomplished man of letters. He, like Edward, represented the protégé of the new, well-rounded man. It was the early dawn of the Renaissance and England's versatile King brought learning and the arts, as well as luxury, to his court.

Richard Plantagenet cared little for jousting tournaments. He was able to skillfully wield an axe and sword, but he lacked the sheer physical bulk that successful jousting demanded. He exercised and practiced martial arts, but to his mind war was serious, not a game. Like Edward and their father, Richard considered military combat to be the last resort when bargaining, arbitration and compromise had run a futile coarse. Loss of life and the tremendous expenditures, which bled treasuries dry, were justifiable only in matters of a grand cause.

Ignoring court intrigue and rumors, Richard preferred to spend his time watching, learning and assisting Edward. However, being thirteen-years-old and with a good mind, Edward found a suitable tutor for his chief admirer. While the Dowager Duchess of York sometimes took Richard with her to Fotheringhay or Canterbury, Richard was for the most part in the company of men. Initially, Richard was acknowledged politely as the King's brother; within a short time, he was accepted for his own worth. Richard earned the reputation of a young man, fiercely loyal to Edward and his family, but conclusively disinterested in the tittle-tattle gossip between feuding elements of the court. He was a congenial comrade, highly principled and an honest lad. More like his father than his brothers.

George, Duke of Clarence, spent most of his time at court. Like other lords, he was present at his estates during planting and harvesting, as he derived a substantial income from his lands. When he was at court, George's quick wit and easy manner made him a man's man as well as a lady's man. George cultivated Richard's friendship and loyalty; that is, when the Duke of Gloucester wasn't at his studies, or with Edward and his ministers. They enjoyed archery, court ball, music and riding together. Richard's childhood veneration of George had not diminished in the slightest. He relished in the sunshine of George's laughter and was honored by the respect George showed him. However, George never told Richard the secret of Edward's father; though at times, he was sorely tempted to knock Edward down a peg or two in Richard's mind. Instead, George kept his clandestine information to himself, not knowing when it would serve him again.

What George and the rest of the court did become increasingly aware of was that Edward IV made no secret of his preference for Richard over George. George was a popular figure in court. However, the King must see something in Richard. Men's attention shifted to Richard so that they might align their affiliations with those of the

King's. Richard was too young and much too busy to notice. He assumed that Edward was spending time with George as well. As for George, he never complained, at least not to Richard.

In July 1465, Warwick found Henry VI on the property of a Lancastrian manor. Totally unaware of his circumstances, Henry VI had few attendants serving him. Warwick brought Henry back to London with his feet tied to his stirrups. Unbeknownst to Henry, he was escorted to the White Tower at the Tower of London. On the one hand, people admired the generosity and kindly nature of the old King. On the other hand, citizens suffered from Henry's inept rule. Those who suffered the most were those who could afford it the least.
Warwick was cheered as he entered London, just as he was applauded everywhere he went. Warwick understood well, the benefits he derived from his generosity and his heroism. He thought the recognition paid him was due solely to his own endeavors. What Warwick failed to wrap his mind around was the fact that Edward's popularity was genuine. Warwick basked in the warmth of the York sun. His vanity would not tolerate the truth. The other matter eluding Warwick was the necessity for real reform.
Warwick turned his attention away from Edward IV to the wooing of the Plantagenet princes. Clarence was an easy conquest. Warwick simply listened sympathetically. It was Warwick who watered and tended the seed of possibility in George's mind that the Duke of Clarence would make a better king than Edward. They became inseparable companions, conspiring surreptitiously. When George approached Edward to ask his permission so that he might marry Warwick's oldest daughter, Isabel, Edward caustically told him, "No!" Edward had no intention of allowing his blackmailer to gain an upper hand through such an advantageous marriage. Did George consider him a fool?

"Never mind, Clarence," consoled Warwick, "The appropriate opportunity will come. When it does we will take hold of the moment and work it to our advantage."

People called Warwick the Kingmaker. He took the title seriously! What Warwick was unwilling to see was the role that Edward's generalship and personal magnetism played in his ascension to the throne. To Warwick's mind, it was entirely through his consent that Edward Plantagenet became Edward IV. He was now determined that George and Isabel would be England's next sovereigns. He thought that he would be able to control George, who would be infinitely more grateful than Edward.

Warwick was absolutely confident in his ability to pull off a usurpation of the throne. He felt that his popularity and authority outshone Edward's. Wherever Warwick went, people shouted out his name. The fact that a small bloc of magnates controlled Henry VI had never been an issue for Warwick. The problem was that it was not he who managed the King. Though Warwick hated the Queen and the Woodvilles intently, he was unwilling to divulge his intensions quite yet. Duplicity served him best. He placated the Queen and feigned reverence with platitudes that went over her head. He treated her kin with deference. To all outward appearances, he was the loyal subject of the Crown.

With Clarence neatly secured in one pocket, Warwick turned to the Duke of Gloucester, whom he knew from the start would be a harder sell. He considered the problem, "Richard is steadfast to Edward IV - all of England knows this! But Richard also feels a immense debt of gratitude to me and my family."

To manage the seduction of Richard, Warwick planned a great festivity and an opulent banquet to commemorate George Neville's appointment as

Archbishop of York. Warwick understood the obligation of his peerage and the personal benefits of generosity. This particular banquet, however, was to be extraordinary. George, Duke of Clarence, would remain absent, affording Warwick the opportunity to fully appeal to Richard.

Richard sat at the table with the Nevilles. The Neville women knew how to charm. Verbosely, they turned their flattery on him. Adamantly, they interjected reminders that he was considered to be an intimate member of the family. Reminiscently, they carefully recapped how the Earl of Warwick had treated Richard like his own son. Even nine-year-old Anne had been meticulously coached; she mused over Richard's last trip to York with the family. When Warwick determined that the young prince was ripe for the picking, he sat next to Richard. With a slight nod of Warwick's head, everyone else took heed and conveniently departed. "Richard, you are looking good, my lad! We miss your company here at Middleham."

"I consider this home!"

"Richard, have you heard that the King has refused to allow Clarence to marry Isabel?"

"Yes, and once Edward has set his mind, it is difficult to change it." Believing that this was the reason behind all of the attention accorded him and anxious to offer Warwick some conciliation, Richard added, "If you wish for me to speak on behalf of George and Isabel, I will do my best, but I am able to offer you no promises."

"Let's put that matter aside. I have not invited you here to discuss the Duke of Clarence."

Richard breathed a sigh of relief. "You have outdone yourself with this amazing feast in honor of your brother."

Warwick had already noticed the Prince's fine, new clothes. Richard wore a deep burgundy, velvet tunic, trimmed in gold thread with jewels sewn into the collar and cuffs. A silver garter, designating his membership in the Order of the

Garter, was worn over his black tights. "This is a hopeful sign! The young henchman is acquiring worldly tastes," thought Warwick to himself. He laughed out loud, "People wonder how it is possible for me to continue to outdo myself. I always will, you know! It gives me great pleasure to surprise and provide for those who are close to me."

"Your brother will make a fine Archbishop."

Warwick acknowledged Richard's statement with a, "Yes!" and then abruptly brought the direction of their tête-à-tête back to marriage, adding in a healthy dose of politics. "I have another daughter. I know the two of you were friends when you lived as a beloved member of my family in this very household. If you were to marry Anne and Clarence married Isabel, you and Clarence would be a force that Edward would be unable to ignore." Warwick assessed Richard's unspoken response and upped the stakes, "You know that it is within my power to grant Anne the bulk of my estates."

Richard was both honored and dismayed at Warwick's proposal. Royal marriages sometimes involved a young girl of considerable means and station, but it was a union in name only until she reached maturity. Warwick's offer was a compliment, but the proposal should have been made initially to the King. There was also something in Warwick's tone. Richard's instincts rose to the surface. He sensed the tip of Warwick's seething anger towards Edward. Not wishing to offend the man he looked upon as a second father, or come between Warwick and Edward, Richard searched his mind. Too stunned by his realization to give a proper a response, Richard blurted out, "If Edward will not permit George to marry Isabel, he won't consent to my marrying Anne."

"The King favors you!"

"I am the King's man, that is all! I would not knowingly displeasure my brother!"

101

"Your union with Anne Neville will strengthen the crown."

It was awkward and objectionable, the thought of being married, and to a young girl whom he would have to wait a considerable number of years for! "I am not ready to take on the responsibilities of a family of my own."

Warwick knew Richard's resolve, but being equally determined, Warwick played his trump card. "Are you aware that Edward is a bastard? He is not the son of the Duke of York!"

Flabbergasted, Richard retorted, "No, I have not heard this gossip. Who speaks treason?"

"The sweet dew of truth came from your mother's own lips!"

"She has never said anything of this to me. When did she say this?"

"After hearing of Edward's marriage."

Richard relaxed a bit. "My mother dislikes Elizabeth Woodville!" Rationalizing that someone surely had twisted angry words spoken by his mother, Richard dismissed Warwick's statements as exaggerations.

Warwick exhausted all avenues of persuasion. When he was truly convinced that the Duke of Gloucester's loyalties were in Edward's camp, he dropped the conversation. An uneasy silence prevailed. Richard inhaled deeply and blew out his anguish. Warwick smiled politely, "Let us find my brother, John. I know that he would like to speak with you. He is a great admirer of King Edward and yourself." Richard liked John Neville and welcomed the ensuing change in conversation.

On February 11, 1466, Queen Elizabeth gave birth to Princess Elizabeth. The ensuing baptism and celebrations went far beyond pomp and protocol. It was a ritual specifically designed for the gratification of the narcissist Queen. Elizabeth's ladies-in-waiting and her own mother spent the entire celebration either on their knees or standing in silent adoration of the newest royal. No one dared to say anything to Edward, who allowed Elizabeth her eccentricities, choosing not to see her acute vanity.

In 1467, Edward told the Commons, "I propose to live off my own means and not to tax my subjects, except in grand and urgent causes." Henry VI owed more money than he was worth. To cover these debts and make the Crown solvent, Edward confiscated lands that the weak King had freely apportioned out or sold for a mere pittance to Lancastrian lords. The disenfranchised lords convulsed in fits of rage! Edward managed his resolution by Act of Parliament. Both the House of Lords and House of Commons were grateful to be free of the King's taxes. As an additional measure to keep the royal household solvent and independent, Edward tried his hand at trade. Soon he was exporting wool and woolen cloth at a handsome profit. Shrewdly, he improved the welfare of all of the merchants by signing trade treaties with Castile, Denmark, Hanse towns and Portugal.

Edward's pleasure was momentary! When the Earl of Worcester was appointed the new Deputy Lieutenant of Ireland, he conspired with the Queen so that she might have her revenge against Desmond. Desmond was accused on false charges. When he arrived in Dublin to defend himself, he was thrown into prison. Queen Elizabeth borrowed Edward's signet to seal Desmond's death warrant. Shortly after he was beheaded, his two young sons were murdered.
News of Desmond's fate was brought to Edward's attention by courier from Ireland. Livid, he stormed out of the Great Hall to seek out the Queen. Finding Elizabeth in her apartments, he heatedly waved everyone out of the room. "Leave! I have business with the Queen." No one had ever seen the affable King in a state

of total distress, not even in battle. Everyone scurried in haste for the door! Unflinchingly, Edward confronted his wife. With an enormous booming voice he asked, "What were you thinking? Desmond meant you no harm. Certainly his sons were innocent. What possible good has their blood brought to you?"

Elizabeth was cornered and she knew it. She had neither thought the consequences of her actions through, nor had she anticipated Edward's rage. Querulously, she responded, "I did not order the death of his children!" It was not her fault! She had only made the suggestion that his family suffer for his imprudent and cheeky comments as to whom Edward should have married.

The long, boisterous argument reverberated through the halls outside the chamber. When Edward at last burst through the doors, those standing scattered. Only the guards, who wished they were in a position to run off as well, remained at the door. Edward failed to notice. From then on, Edward made little secret of his affairs and visited the Queen's bedchambers a little less frequently. Reports of the royal couple's row raced rapidly throughout the realm.

The Queen was ruffled. Why hadn't her husband defended her honor, rather than stand by a dead man who thought Edward would have been better off marrying a princess from the Continent? For that matter, why did he seek out other women when he had her? Edward's callous affairs had been n affront to her honor. However, she found her own way to mend and sooth her ego with her own secret liaisons. If only she could tell Edward! She would hurt him as he had injured her. Then her pride would be restored to its full grandeur.

That same spring, ambassadors from France and Burgundy, each with an impressive marriage contract, gifts and lucrative trade agreements, arrived at Westminster. The French, with high hopes, departed for their homeland first, in the company of Warwick. Duke Philip, who had turned the reins of government over to his son, Charles, several years before, died while the Burgundy contingency was in London. As they hastily made arrangements to return for Duke Philip's prearranged elaborate funeral, Edward learned that Louis XI was ready to annex Burgundy. Prevention was only possible if England entered European Continental politics on the side of Burgundy.

Spinning a net of praise and promise, Louis XI, Father of Flattery, caught Warwick smack in the middle of it. Warwick returned to London gripped in another outbreak of the Black Plague. He sought out Edward. To his consternation and outrage, he was informed that Edward had failed to sign the French treaty. To Warwick's humiliation, Edward had signed an alliance with Henry of Castile against France. If that wasn't enough, Warwick's spies informed him that the Queen was encouraging Edward to marry his sister, Princess Margaret, to Charles of Burgundy. Livid, Warwick returned to Middleham. He called for an assemblage of his brothers and included the Duke of Clarence. Much to Warwick's dismay, John Neville announced that he wasn't coming. He would stand by King Edward. Without the Earl of Northumberland, Warwick would have to bide his time.

When he was no longer able to reap the benefits of procrastination, forced to make a decision one way or the other, Edward chose Burgundy. Trade with Burgundy was an important aspect of London merchants' business. Englishmen were still deeply humiliated that Henry VI was unable to hold onto French territory. Edward's subjects would not stomach an English alliance with France! In March 1468, when Edward could defer no longer, he ratified the marriage treaty between Charles of Burgundy and Princess Margaret.

To further strengthen his position, Edward signed a treaty with Francis, Duke of Brittany. In June, Margaret set off on her wedding journey to Margate accompanied by her three brothers, Warwick and leading lords of the land.

The Plantagenets and their party returned to an England, knee deep in a flurry of intrigue. One of Queen Margaret's spies had been caught. Under torture, he implicated friends and associates of Warwick. Edward mistrusted information gleaned from torture — it too often proved unreliable! Still willing to put his convictions in Warwick, he sent Warwick and Clarence to investigate the insurrection.

Simultaneously, Louis sponsored an assault on the Welsh coast. Led by Jasper Tudor, claiming to be the Earl of Pembroke, his forces burned Denbigh. Lord William Herbert and his brother responded by routing the Lancastrian forces. Capturing the last Lancaster castle, they forced Jasper Tudor to flee for France. Edward quickly realized that the allegations were true. Warwick was involved in treason. For his victory, Lord Herbert was elevated to Earl of Pembroke.

Margaret Beaufort had married Sir Henry Stafford, a Lancastrian knight. Her ten-year-old son, Henry Tudor, had been under the guardianship of William Herbert since 1461. In that year, Lord Herbert had taken Pembroke Castle. When he and his men searched the fortress, they discovered Henry Tudor in the castle's keep. Lord Herbert and his wife took a liking to Henry. Opening their hearts to him, they treated Henry like a son and saw to his education. It was intended that Henry would someday marry their daughter, Maud, whom fortune now smiled upon. Henry Tudor's fate and fortune appeared secure. However, letters from his mother served to remind Henry of her ambitions for him.

Witches Brew
and Cauldrons Bubble

In the North troubles began early in 1469. Robin of Redsdale led a rebellion that was quickly put down by the Earl of Northumberland. Shortly, Robin of Holderness headed yet another uprising. No sooner had John Neville defeated the rebels and killed their leader, when Robin of Redsdale reappeared.

Clarence used the opportunity to play his trump card. He imprudently began telling a few trusted individuals that Edward was a bastard and that he, the Duke of Clarence, was the rightful king of England. Soon the rumor was spreading.

Edward assembled a small contingency of men in June. At the last minute, he included Richard. They headed north, procrastinating along the way. Edward was too busy to ignore the signs throughout England. In Bedfordshire it rained blood, which stained grass and soaked laundry hanging out to dry. A wise woman in Huntington heard her unborn child weeping. Several people in different parts of the realm reported seeing a mounted knight in the skies leading men in arms.

Edward thought that Warwick was guarding England's southern coast. Yes, Warwick was at sea! However, he was escorting Clarence and Isabel to Calais, where George Neville married the couple on July 11th.

By the time Edward realized that Robin of Redsdale was leading a significant army, much larger than his own, his only option was to retreat to Nottingham. Safe in the fortress, he sent word to William Herbert to marshal forces and come to his aid. At the same time, Warwick landed in England with an army. Heading north to join

Robin of Redsdale, Warwick encountered Pembroke, who was on his way to help Edward. Pembroke found himself in the unfortunate predicament of being caught between Robin of Redsdale and Warwick. The two armies annihilated Pembroke's forces. Pembroke was captured and beheaded.

Edward, artful as well as courageous, understood full well how to cut his loses short, and when to retreat to reorganize. Without hesitation, he dispersed his small army. Gathering the Woodvilles, John Howard, William Hastings and Richard around him, he gave his orders, "They will find me alone and unarmed. They will not risk the shame of harming me. Go! Go and marshal forces! Public opinion will turn against the traitors. You will know when it is time to rescue me."

The Woodvilles left at once. Richard lingered; William Hastings and John Howard stood nearby. "I will remain with you, just like I stayed with our mother and George at Ludlow."

"Hastings will go to Lancashire where he will muster forces. You will go to Northumberland to raise an army."

"Warwick may murder you in the same manner Lord Herbert was slain.

"Should he be so rash, you must live, little brother. Go before it is too late! All of you!"

The Archbishop of York arrived several hours later. Accolades of victory had been snatched from his grasp; Edward was alone and unarmed. The Archbishop dared not risk condemnation by slaying the King. His only recourse was to escort the amenable Edward to Coventry to confront Clarence and Warwick, where Edward conceded agreeably to his brother and uncle's demands.

Warwick and Clarence's forces routed a royal force intended to free Edward. Earl Rivers, Sir John Woodville, the Earl of Devon and Thomas Herbert were captured and beheaded. The insurgents' confidence grew.

To secure Edward, Warwick and Clarence moved him to Middleham Castle before they left for London in August. In the great city news of King Edward's imprisonment brought day-to-day life to a squealing halt. Mob violence loomed; disorder, injustice prevailed. Further uncertainty was added to the brew when the Duke of Burgundy pledged aid and troops to free Edward. John Neville, Earl of Northumberland, refused to help his brothers. When Warwick attempted to marshal men to arms for the purpose of putting down a Lancastrian uprising, not one man answered his call. "Not until Edward was freed!" they cried.

The Archbishop responded by escorting the King to Pontefract Castle. Not long afterwards, Edward received news that Richard and Hastings, along with their forces, were converging on Pontefract. Edward instinctively knew the time had come for action. He called members of his Council to assemble. The King's men hastily responded, gathering around him like a comfortable cloak. Edward made an announcement to his captors, "The Duke of Gloucester and Lord Hastings have arrived to escort the lords and myself to London."

Backed into a position whereby he could do nothing to prevent their departure, the Archbishop of York's only option was to allow Edward to leave. In the courtyard the King looked about and asked, "Where is my horse?"

Grudgingly, George Neville handed over one of his own mounts. Edward smiled broadly as he rode across the drawbridge. York's great sun banner and throngs of cheering, loyal men greeted him. Edward's heart swelled! He spied Richard, who was dressed in a full-suit of armor at the head of his troops. Honor filled Richard's being as Edward caught his eye and nodded approvingly.

It was the end of September, when King Edward and his company rode into London. Trumpet fanfares and thundering cheers greeted them. Women wept for joy; city officials were decked out in their finest ceremonial garb. Carrying his helmet under his arm, Richard allowed his fatigued horse to stretch out his neck. His steed seemed to know that a fresh bed of straw, a bin of hay and a large scoop of oats awaited him. Richard unearthed a new surge of energy from the comradery and enthusiasm surrounding him. Soon his mind returned to weightier matters.

Not long after the jubilation of securing Edward's liberty, Richard's thoughts despondently returned to George and Warwick. Warwick was like a second father. Could Warwick and George be persuaded to return to Edward's government? Would he be able to convince Edward to grant clemency? Would the Queen ask Edward to grant her revenge for the beheading of her father and brother; a carnal act ordered by Warwick and George? After all, the Queen had Desmond executed for making an unintentional slight to her person, what vengeance would she seek for homicide?

When the party reached Windsor Castle's stables, Richard quietly dismounted, leaving his charger to the grooms. His squire proceeded to help him remove layers of armor. First off were pauldrons that covered Richard's shoulders, coutes over his elbows, poleyns for knee defense and sabatons worn over his shoes. Off came vambraces covering his upper and lower arms, cuisses covering his thighs, and breaves protecting his shins and calves. Breast and back plates were heavier. The double of mail, which had been affixed to the plate armor, left impressions on his shirt and skin. Cuirass, with laminated metal plates below the waist, from which hung tassets that overlapped the cuisses were removed. At long last Richard was left standing in his linen shirt, underdrawers, woolen hose and leather shoes.

Word came to him while his armor was being removed that his former lover wished to speak with him. His squire helped Richard to clean up and change into clothes suitable for court. Sending his squire away, Richard sat down at his finely carved desk and chair to glance over ledgers of his estates that his accountant, Thomas Metcalfe, had prepared for him. On the white plaster walls hung several tapestries, the largest being an elaborate depiction of the siege of Troy. Smaller tapestries venerated Saint Catherine and Saint Ninian — both of whom were popular in the North of England. His many, often-read books included a Bible. Certainly, not as elaborate as King Edward's apartments, but princely, nonetheless.

A Yeoman knocked on the door. Lady Eleanor was announced and escorted into his apartment. Richard stood to greet her. He was glad to see that she had brought his baby daughter, Katherine. "Eleanor, how are you?"

"I am well thank you, and you?" Eleanor handed Katherine to Richard, who gingerly grappled, trying to adjust her to a comfortable position. Katherine was not yet one. She already resembled Cecily and Margaret. Eleanor smiled, "She won't break, Richard!"

Their affair had ended, but not before Eleanor had become pregnant. It was his first real test of chivalry; he made the choice to support Eleanor and his daughter. He spent what little time he was able to spare with Katherine. "Do you have enough?"

"I am betrothed to a young courtier. It would be beneficial to have additional funds so that we could live on our own."

Richard could not marry Eleanor himself. The King and council would never permit him to enter into wedlock beneath his station. Edward had pushed the lords' patients to the limit! Richard had had feelings for Eleanor, but it was not the great love characterized in the books, which George and he had read. However, Richard's generosity made Eleanor a desirable catch, and her marriage would insure that Katherine would have a stable upbringing in a comfortable household. "I will speak with Metcalfe."

Pardons and peace were proffered to all participants in Warwick's short-lived coup d'état. Despite the Queen's urgings, Warwick and Clarence were included. Furthermore, to the Queen's dismay, Edward relieved her brother, Lord Scales, of his father's post as Constable of England. With the death of his father and by right of birth, Anthony Rivers was elevated to Lord Rivers.

Edward expanded the duties of Constable to include the President of the Court of Chivalry and of Courts Martial. For Richard's service and loyalty, Edward appointed him Constable of England for life. In addition, Richard was granted Sudeley Castle and surrounding land.

Not two months after Richard's appointment, an uprising occurred in Wales. Chipping away at Warwick's Welsh dominance, Edward appointed the Duke of Gloucester the Chief Justice of North Wales. Before the month of November was over, Richard was made Chief Steward, Approver and Surveyor of Wales. He was granted the Earldom of March and Edmund's former estates.

Before Christmas, Richard and his army subdued and captured the Welsh rebels, who were raiding and pillaging the country. Richard and his men reclaimed the castles the insurgents had held. After swearing an oath of allegiance to the Saxon King, Edward, Richard granted the rebels pardons and set them free. Richard was back in London for the holidays. Edward was impressed! He had put his trust in the right man!

Richard found pleasure in court festivities and his newest lover. However, his leisure was fleeting. Another Welsh uprising sent Richard back to Wales. In January 1470, Richard received further appointments, including the Chief Justice of South Wales, effectively creating him the viceroy of Wales. Thus, categorically bringing Warwick to heel.

In a somewhat conciliatory gesture to Warwick, but in effect rewarding John Neville, Edward signed a contract of betrothal between Princes Elizabeth and John Neville's young son. In addition, Edward created him Duke of Bedford. Edward used the ceremony to sign a general pardon for any who had been involved in riots or insurrection prior to Christmas. Edward also took back all lands, titles and offices that Warwick and Clarence had forced him to sign over to them during his captivity.

Winter's cold grasp was still upon the realm when there occurred an uprising in Lincolnshire. Rebels demanded that Henry VI be reinstated as king. Warwick rode to the Midlands, promising to restore order. Clarence joined him. On March 6, the King, the Earl of Arundel, Lord Hastings and Henry Percy rode to Waltham Abbey. Once they arrived, a courier brought word that on Sunday, a call to arms against the King had been included in every sermon in Lincolnshire. Edward sent word back to London requesting reinforcements. With Wales solidly under Richard's control, Edward dispatched commissions of array to Warwick and Clarence at Waltham. Edward watched to see what transpired.

Two of the conspirators, Welles and Dymmock, sought out the King, confident of a pardon. Instead, Edward informed them, "General pardon was issued for treason committed prior to Christmas. Welles, unless you persuade your son and his army to surrender, you and Dymmock will be executed." Terrified, Welles wrote to his son as Edward's army pressed on.

At Fotheringhay, Edward's concerned mother greeted him warmly. Cecily's guard had discovered that Sir Robert Welles had cut off any possible retreat to London. At Stamford, Edward received a dispatch from Warwick and Clarence, stating that they were on their way to help. Hardly had the courier dismounted when Edward's scouts entered the city at full gallop. Dismounting hurriedly, they were rushed to the King. "Your Majesty, Sir Robert has swung his men around to the north end of Stamford and are preparing a surprise attack."

Edward turned to a captain, "See to it that Welles and Dymmock are taken to the block!"

Quickly assembling his army, Edward's forces routed the rebels, who discarded their telltale jackets as they fled the scene. Papers were found on a slain body, which turned out to be the remains of one of Clarence's servants, confirming George's involvement. The captured Sir Robert confirmed evidence found on the field, "Warwick and Clarence planned the uprising to depose Edward and crown the Duke of Clarence, George I."

Edward continued marching north, while Warwick and Clarence marched in the same direction, but 35 miles to the west. They exchanged dispatches as their armies moved. Warwick and Clarence promised allegiance to Edward, but failed to show up when Edward commanded them to appear before him. Leaving the Earl of Northumberland to deal with insurgents in York, Edward pursued Warwick and Clarence. Before reaching them, Edward was forced to turn his army back towards York for supplies. On March 23rd, the King proclaimed his brother and Warwick traitors.

When Edward's army arrived in the city, he learned that John Neville had put down the insurrection and was bringing the traitors to him for pardons. Wales and Northumberland remained like cauldrons, brewing up rebels and rebellion, one after the other. Yielding to pressure to restore peace to the north, and against the advice of Richard of Gloucester, Edward relieved John Neville of the princely earldom and estates of Northumberland. Henry Percy was reinstated as Earl of Northumberland. The former earl was made

114

Marquisate of Montagu. It was a small substitute and a dreadful insult for his steadfast support of the King over his own brothers.

When Richard learned that George had been declared a traitor and that Edward was heading north, he left Wales in the hands of his captains. Gathering a small force, Richard set out to help Edward. Instinctively, he took the Hereford-Shrewsbury road. Just south of Cheshire, Richard learned that Lord Stanley was supporting Warwick and Clarence. Stanley's men, having been summoned to arms, were throughout Cheshire. Stanley himself was gathering more troops in Manchester. Rapidly, Richard disbanded his troops. They proceeded individually and in pairs stealthily around Cheshire. Reassembling north of the city, they forged ahead. Richard sent a messenger to Edward to warn him of Stanley's betrayal and assure him that help was on the way. Richard continued on to Manchester, where he dispersed Stanley's men.

Warwick and Clarence maneuvered to attack Edward, but wisely waited for Stanley's troops to arrive. Stanley, however, had a change of heart. Brusquely, he sent one message to Warwick stating that he was not coming; another dispatch to the King protested the Duke of Gloucester's roughing up his men. Richard joined up with Edward, and together they set off to catch Warwick and Clarence, who were retreating south with their families. They managed to reach the sea before Edward and Richard could catch them.

The port of Calais was closed to Warwick and his family. Isabel, forced to endure child labor in a cramped cabin with only her mother and sister assisting her, gave birth to a weak, sickly infant, who survived for only a few hours. Normandy was Warwick's only port of entry where of Louis XI readily waited with outstretched arms.

On July 22, after immense difficulty, Louis managed to reconcile Queen Margaret and Warwick.

Three days later, the 16-year-old Prince of Wales married 15-year-old Anne Neville, a pretty, blond, petite girl. The boastful Prince Edward, truly a product of his environment, haughtily and incessantly spoke in great and gory details of how he would vanquish his enemies. His passion for hostilities rivaled that of Mars, god of war.

Edward spent the summer of 1470 preparing for Warwick's invasion. Richard raised troops in the Midlands. Earl Rivers, Lord Howard and a fleet from Burgundy blocked the French coasts. Spies were dispatched to the Continent. On the pretext of joining Clarence's household, a brave young woman was sent to encourage the Duke of Clarence to return to his family.

Montagu and Northumberland were unable to put down an uprising in York. Edward sent Richard, who succeeded. For his service, Richard was appointed to the post that Warwick had long held — Warden of the West Marches.

In September, Edward joined Richard in York so as to cut Warwick off from his support. However, Warwick had other plans. On September 9th, a gale scattered Edward's blockade, affording Warwick and Jasper Tudor the opportunity to sail for England in French vessels, provided by Louis XI. Supporting the uneasy alliance, were the armies mustered by the Earl of Oxford, the Earl of Shrewsbury, Lord Stanley and John Neville, the disgruntled former Earl of Northumberland. Learning of Montagu's defection and being sorely outnumbered, Edward gathered his mounted men. Along with Richard, Hastings and Anthony, Earl Rivers, Edward galloped east in the middle of the night. Securing small vessels, they sailed for Burgundy.

The voyage was rough! The sea heaved their vessels about, as if they were bobbles! It took two men to hold the wheel of the ship. Those on deck were mindful not to be washed overboard. Men without sea legs chucked up what little they had managed to eat before setting out. Edward and his men barely managed to keep their ships afloat. Pirates were sighted; the buccaneers hunted them on the seas. Fate intervened! Dutch sentinels spotted Edward's English banners as well as their pursuers. Louis of Burges, Governor of Holland for Charles, Duke of Burgundy, intervened. His forces rescued Edward and his men at the eleventh hour.

Edward, Richard, Hastings and Rivers remained secured at the Governor's mansion in Bruges while waiting for an audience with the Duke of Burgundy. In typical form, Edward refused to give in to fear or worry. His calm and stalwart nature imparted confidence to his men, whom Edward made certain were quartered comfortably nearby.

Henry VI, a bit rough and crusty around the edges from his confinement, was released from the Tower and trotted out as King of the new Lancastrian government. Henry's hair had long since turned white; his beard had been left to grow while in the solitude of his cell. Most people who saw the old King questioned if Henry knew what was happening. Ever since his personal physician had drilled the hole in his skull to let out the poison of insanity, Henry had never been quite right.

Warwick at last had his way! He had complete control over a mad sovereign, who was wholly incapable of decision-making or ruling. Louis XI was delighted with his new alliance with England. Warwick hadn't mentioned to the Council or Parliament as yet, that Burgundy and Brittany were being thrown to the wolves. Queen Margaret remained in France. Having a propensity for being cautious at the wrong moment, she waited to sail for England.

George, Duke of Clarence, was the epitome of a round peg in a square hole! He had not become a turncoat to be an obscure York lord in a Lancastrian reign. He dared not disclose his displeasure. However, George was not entirely left without friends. The diocese of Robert Stillington, Bishop of Bath and Wells, lay within the Duke of Clarence's holdings. Secretly, the Bishop urged George to return to his family.

Jasper Tudor proudly brought his nephew to court to meet the King. When the thirteen-year-old Henry Tudor was introduced to Henry VI, the King exclaimed, "This is he whom we and our adversaries must yield to and give over dominion."

George Plantagenet was also at court that day. When the personable young Henry was introduced to the Duke of York, the boy took an immediate disliking to George. Distain the adolescent felt was easily read on his face. Initially embarrassed, Jasper Tudor recovered. After all, George was a son of York! What was he doing in Henry VI's court anyway?

The lad's glance did not pass by George unnoticed. George, too, was wondering why he was in Henry VI's court. He had had more power in Edward IV's court. Warwick had lost interest in him! Queen Margaret's son was now next in line to the throne. Under these circumstances, the most George could hope for was brother-in-law to the Queen.

The Dowager Duchess of York was safe for the moment, at Baynard's Castle. Queen Elizabeth, along with several of her ladies-in-waiting, had been forced to seek sanctuary at Westminster Abbey. In a more lucid moment, Henry VI learned of Elizabeth's plight and took pity upon her. Henry ordered food and wine sent to Elizabeth and those accompanying her. On November 2nd, Elizabeth gave birth to Prince Edward. Though the boy had a rare bone disease in his jaw, there were many in England who found this a hopeful sign.

Will the Real King of England Please Stand Up

Charles, Duke of Burgundy, held off receiving Edward and his party. Though his wife was from the House of York, Charles still favored the Lancastrians. He was hoping to cultivate mutually favorable relations with the new English government. Ah, illusions are short lived! Hard facts have a way of impinging upon reality with impact so that delusions, left without weight, shatter and scatter, leaving one wondering how the old beliefs ever held sway. Only a fool or one thoroughly entrenched in dogma, insulated and impervious to contrary opinion, would continue on a crumbling road. In December, Louis XI declared war on Burgundy! England was France's ally!

Cordially and demonstratively, Charles received Edward and his captains. Reluctantly, Charles provided Edward with money, aid and troops. Edward began preparations for invasion. Messengers carried letters to loyal York supporters.

On March 11, 1471, Edward made sail for Yorkshire, believing that the Lancastrian coasts would be unguarded. However, a sudden squall came up, tossing and separating the fleet. At long last, Richard spotted shore, but the other vessels had long been out of sight. Richard and his men disembarked in the middle of a chilly, rainy night. Richard took comfort in the fact that his brother's estimation of the situation was correct; no Lancastrian sentries had been stationed. Still, he ordered his men not to make unnecessary noise while they unloaded the shaken horses and supplies. The camp forwent fires. Richard at last focused his attention to the earth beneath him. "North or south? Where had Edward landed?" He went to sleep with the question on his mind.

In the morning, Richard's gut feeling told him that Edward's party was located to the south. Breaking camp, he led his men to Ravenspur, where Henry Bolingbroke had landed with his force in 1399, and went on to take the crown from Richard II. Much relieved, the Duke of Gloucester found Edward and his men in Ravenspur.

Edward led his army northwest to York, where wary citizens allowed them to spend the night. The next morning, Edward marched south through Northumberland. Percy showed his gratitude to the King for the restoration of his title by doing nothing. He allowed Edward to pass unharmed. Montagu, on the other hand, had gathered a large force at Pontefract. Edward worked his men around the blockade, forging on to Sandal Castle and reinforcements. Montagu could not bring himself to attack; he simply trailed behind Edward.

Men in arms joined Edward's ranks while enemy forces encroached upon him. Montagu persisted at Edward's rear; Warwick lay waiting in front him at Coventry; the Earl of Oxford rode on his flank to the east. Demonstrating superb generalship abilities, Edward attacked Oxford with alacrity and vigor, forcing Oxford to retreat.

On the road to Coventry, Edward picked up more retainers. At Coventry, Edward declared himself King but Warwick refused to come out to either fight or accept a pardon. Instead, Warwick waited for Montagu, Oxford and the Duke of Clarence, who was marching with a large force from the southeast. Choosing not to wait for George's arrival, Edward and Richard rode south to meet their wayward brother.

George's scouts had already assessed him of the entire situation. Waiting at the head of his army with two of his captains, George's course of action had been predetermined. Edward and Richard were spotted! George and a few of his men rode out alone to greet them. Dismounting and throwing himself on his knees in front of Edward, George pleaded for mercy. Edward grabbed George by his arms, vigorously lifting him to his feet. Edward kissed him and heartily threw his arms around George's shoulders. The prodigal brother had returned home! Richard's heart swelled.

George and Edward rallied their men. The following morning, Edward converged upon Warwick, still behind the city walls. George was given a generous peace accord and pardon with which to offer Warwick. Warwick, incensed and blinded by will and hatred, turned the Duke of Clarence away. Oxford and Montagu converged upon Coventry. Warwick still refused to come out and fight.

On April 5th, Edward's spies informed him that Queen Margaret and her son were making preparations to return to England. Hoping to force Warwick's hand, before her arrival, Edward changed tactics. He turned his army towards London. Taken completely unaware, Warwick hesitated. His only choice was to take off in pursuit Edward.

Londoners were decidedly in favor of Edward IV. The council, following suit, made preparations to receive the King. On April 11th, Edward marched into London. Hastily assembled trumpeters and elated multitudes greeted him. After ordering Henry VI and the Archbishop of York to the White Tower of London, he proceeded to Westminster Abbey. Tenderly, he consoled his Queen; gently, he held his son. Gathering his family around him, Edward sought momentary sanctuary in Baynard's Castle.

On Holy Saturday of the Holy Easter vigil, King Edward IV assembled his troops at St. John's Field, where many Londoners had gathered to watch. In order to keep an eye on George, Edward kept the Duke of Clarence with him to lead the center guard. Lord Hastings took his position as commander of the rear guard. Edward entrusted the command of the vanguard to eighteen-year-old Prince Richard. The remaining royal captains, Rivers, Howard and Say, took up their positions within the configuration.

Late in the afternoon, the impressive royal forces headed north to meet Warwick. Before sunset, Edward's scouts returned, reporting that at Barnet his advance troops had successfully engaged Warwick's own advance troops. Edward's forces had driven Warwick's soldiers out of the town. When Edward entered Barnet, his scouts informed him that Warwick's entire army lay in ambush behind large hedges on the road only a mile north. Conferring with his captains, Edward laid out his strategy.

Furtively, Edward's army pressed forward under the canopy of a starless night. Cautiously, Richard advanced north on St. Albans road. Before reaching the enemy, he swung off to the heather on the east, in essence becoming Edward's right wing. Edward's center guard pushed forward as close as they dared, forming a line across the road. Hastings extended the left wing to the west along the slope of the plateau.

In the near distance, Richard and his men heard noisy war preparations and comradery of fifteen thousand men, whom Warwick had summoned to Henry VI's cause. Warwick was utterly confident that he would win the upcoming conflict and bury all three of the ungrateful Plantagenet brothers. Assuming that Edward had reached the town of Barnet, Warwick fired his cannons into the town and its outskirts. Cannonballs whistled over the heads of Edward's army; he and his captains bid the soldiers to remain quiet and get what rest they could before tomorrow's battle.

Dense, thick, soupy fog rolled up onto the plateau in the early hours of Easter Sunday. Rising at four o'clock, well before dawn, Edward's men ate a cold breakfast. Afterwards, as per Edward's instructions, the armed, dismounted men assembled in lines facing the enemy. Edward kept his reserves hindermost. Archers clustered at the ends of the flanks. Edward and his captains joined the men-at-arms, fully prepared to do combat. As soon as the King's trumpet's sounded the call to arms, Richard gave the order for archers to fire blindly into the enemy position. Edward ordered the commencement of cannon fire. Richard gave the order, "Advance banner!"

Edward's center clashed hard against Montagu's forces. Hastings prepared to engage Warwick's right flank, Oxford's army. Richard still had not encountered the enemy. Advancing down an abrupt slope and into a marshy bottom, Richard realized that he had outflanked Warwick's left flank. Exeter's men, directly above him on the plateau, were completely unaware of Richard's position. Richard quietly ordered his captains to swing the line so that it faced west. They began the laborious task of climbing up the precipitous incline to the plateau in full suits of armor. Exeter's men faced south. It was as if Richard had cloaked his men; somehow, the enemy was unable to perceive their advance.

Richard reached the top and peered up over the ridge. Before him he saw a line of feet disappearing into the mist. He was still unperceived! When Richard felt confident that the first line of men had reached the edge of the plateau, he gave the order to charge. Quickly hoisting themselves up over the edge, Richard's forces began swinging battleaxes and swords in fierce, brutal hand-to-hand combat, taking out Exeter's line as they advanced forward. Often, it took more than one blow to bring a man down. Fetid odor of death hung in the misty air. Exeter's line became a beehive of confusion. Row by row behind Richard, the vanguard advanced to the top of the plateau to join his ranks. Methodically, Richard advanced his position onto the plateau and further away from the edge.

Exeter's captains scrambled to reassemble their line so that it faced Edward's right flank. Richard and his men aggressively held their ground! Exeter nervously sent a message to Warwick, who was in the rear with the reserves. Warwick mistakenly assumed that Edward's right flank was the bulk of his army. He ordered his reserves to Exeter's line. Exeter's line held.

In the meantime, Oxford outmaneuvered Edward's left flank in the fog, and proceeded to roll through Hasting's line. Hastings men were sent fleeing with Oxford in hot pursuit. To Oxford's dismay, his men stopped in Barnet to pillage. Some of Hasting's men made it to London with news that the Yorkists were defeated and the Plantagenets were dead.

Hastings collected what men he had left and fearlessly fought to Edward's left. Intrepidly, Edward beat and bore down every man in his way, lending courage and strength to his men. During the conflict, the line of battle shifted so that Edward faced northwest. Montagu faced southeast.

Unlike Warwick, Edward had not spent his reserves. Edward sent a scout to reconnoiter Richard's needs. "Are you able to hold without reserves?"

Richard replied, "Yes!" In spite of unbelievable odds, he and his men were holding. Several more times during the course of engagement, Edward asked the same question. Always, the reply was the same! "We are holding!"

Warwick's scouts had kept him informed. Oxford was expected to attack Edward from the rear, after he had chased down the left flank. However, it took Oxford some time to reorganize his looting troops. Confident of crushing Edward between his forces and Montagu's, Oxford rode back towards the battle. The unusually dense miasma obscured one piece of critical information. Oxford was unable to see that the battle line had moved in his absence. Oxford inadvertently attacked

Montagu's forces! Montagu's men mistook Oxford's banner of a star for Edward's banner of a sun and retaliated with a volley of arrows. In the bedlam shouts of "Treason!" were heard from both sides.

While Edward could only guess at what was happening, he perceived a weakness in the centerline in front of him. He seized the moment! Calling up his reserves, Edward crushed into Warwick's center.

Totally unaware of anything that had transpired, Richard, who was wounded slightly, still upheld his position. Suddenly, there was a commotion to his left. A shudder trickled through Exeter's line. As Warwick's centerline collapsed, the effect of disarray continued like a domino effect to Warwick's rear. Richard signaled his trumpeters to sound off the call to advance banners. Summoning newfound energy from a source deep within them, Richard and his men rushed forward, driving across Warwick's rear and slaying the enemy as they progressed. The line convulsed and split! Montagu was dead! Lancastrians and retainers were abandoning the field! Oxford retreated to Scotland! The sounds of combat subsided. Only the groans and cries of the wounded were heard. Surgeons, preparing to cut mortifying flesh and mangled limbs, entered the field. Warwick ran for the horses but was cut down; his cries for succor went unheeded. Edward was not there to intervene.

Richard removed his helmet. An impenetrable haze, combined with the heaviness of death, severely limited visibility. The clank of men-in-arms became audible to his immediate left. Without warning, through the fog, appeared the House of York's illustrious sun banner. Edward's center met up with his right flank! The battle ended at seven o'clock in the morning! As if they were in a world apart, blankets of white clouds surrounded the two brothers and their immediate forces. Edward lifted his visor and grinned! "You've earned your spurs today, little brother!"

Easter Sunday afternoon, long after masses had been said, sermons preached and parishioners paid homage; Edward jubilantly surprised Londoners by marching into the city. The bodies of Warwick and Montagu, clad only in loincloths, were laid on the pavement of St. Paul's. It was the end of the House of Neville!

Easter Sunday afternoon, Queen Margaret, her son, her new daughter-in-law, Anne Neville, and her forces landed at Weymouth. After hearing news of Warwick's defeat, Margaret's first instinct was to run back to France. However, Edmund Beaufort, the Duke of Somerset, and the Earl of Devon eased her discommode. "Edward's victory has left him vulnerable. We are fresh and ready to fight!" Dorset and Wiltshire soon joined Margaret's ranks, bequeathing confidence.

On April 16th, two days after Easter Sunday, Edward's spies informed him that Queen Margaret had landed and was marching to London. Edward sent out a new call of retainer. Soon, fresh forces began arriving at Windsor. On April 23rd, the feast of Saint George, a scout informed Edward's council of war that Margaret's forces had turned. She was headed for Wales! If Margaret made it to her support in Lancashire or Wales, a sizeable force would be summoned to her banners. The following day, Edward resolutely took up the chase.

Edward caught up with the Queen's fagged forces on May 4th, on the outskirts of Tewkesbury. No town had opened its gates to her army. Edward and his men had had the distinct advantage of having townsfolk welcome them with food and drink. Edward conferred with his royal captains. Richard was again assigned commander of the vanguard.

Marching across the field, he took up position as Edward's left flank, facing the Duke of Somerset. Edward followed; his centerline faced Margaret's son and Lord Wentlock. Hastings led the rear guard into the position of Edward's right flank. Surveying the rough terrain between Richard and Somerset, Edward stationed 200 spearmen a few hundred yards to Richard's left.

Neither Richard nor Somerset was able to get close enough to engage hand-to-hand combat. Between the two armies were foul lanes, deep dykes and scores of wild, high hedges. Both commanders turned to their archers. Volleys of arrows, like swarms of hornets, sped through the air. Cannonballs shrilled and exploded upon impact. Using the tall hedges for cover, Somerset boldly maneuvered his men, succeeding in outflanking Richard. Somerset gave the order to advance arms. Edward's left flank, however, was not unnerved! Richard and his captains quickly and adeptly reassembled their men to face Somerset. Richard signaled to one of his scouts. "Take this order to the spearmen. They are to attack Somerset's rear guard. The spearmen are to make as much noise as possible. They are to make Somerset think that another army is charging down upon him!"

The scout took off. Richard signaled his marshaled troops to attack. The intensity of Richard's attack took Somerset off guard. His line moved back. Just then, two hundred spearmen, following Richard's instructions, came yelping, whooping and howling onto the enemy as if they were banshees from an abyss. Somerset's line faltered, then retreated in panic. Spearmen slew the enemy as they ran; others headed for the River Avon. However, the tributary was deeper than expected. Many drowned in the attempted crossing!

Edward signaled his center to charge into Wentlock and the Prince. Richard swung his line around to outflank Queen Margaret's centerline. He called the order to advance arms.

In the heat of the battle, the furious Somerset found Wentlock. "What the bloody hell is the matter with you? Why didn't you support my attack on Edward's left flank?" Lifting his battleaxe, he took a swing at Wentlock's head. This was too much for the majority of the Lancastrian men-in-arms. They took flight! Hastings and his men pursued like dogs, chasing a deer. Prince Edward ran for the abbey along with other Lancastrians, but the Duke of Clarence caught up with the Prince before he reached sanctuary. "Assist me!" Pleaded Prince Edward!

"Take up your sword and fight!"

It was no contest! George cut Margaret's son down with the first blow of his sword. The Lancastrian hope lay dead. Edward blasted his way past George to confront the abbot.

"Good King, I implore you to honor the sanctuary of this holy place."

Edward conceded to the abbot's request. "I beg your pardon." A few Lancastrians more or less would not matter. Perhaps, they would remember his act of clemency?

One of Edward's men hastened to his side. "A moment, Sire!" Edward nodded for him to speak. "Somerset and his captains are in the abbey."

Edward was unable to put aside Somerset's treachery. On May 2nd, Somerset and twelve others were forcefully taken from the abbey and tried before the Constable of England, the Duke of Gloucester. All were found guilty of treason and beheaded in Tewkesbury. Four days later, William Stanley attained Margaret of Anjou in a nearby convent on the other side of the river Severn. She was overwhelmingly devastated by news of the death of her son. With her was Anne Neville, too confounded to mourn. George kindly intervened on Anne's behalf, charging several of his men to safely escort Anne to his wife, Isabel, in London.

Londoners and those from neighboring and distant towns turned out in euphoric rejoicing, to welcome Edward IV's army as they entered the city on May 21st. The Duke of Gloucester proudly led the procession! Trumpet fanfares, clarions, fluttering banners overhead and shouts of, "Long live King Edward IV!" filled the air.

Later, Edward met with his advisors. In front of him on the table was an unsigned execution order. "With Margaret's son dead, we are in a position to execute Henry VI. He does, however, have a following among the people. What is your position?"

Hastings spoke up, "The people will be happier when civil strife is put to an end!"

Norfolk added, "Many are expecting this. Henry's execution will not come as a shock."

Edward looked to Howard, "Henry's harmless enough, but so long as he lives, we run the risk of fanatical followers stirring up trouble."

"What say you Rivers?"

"Henry's name inspires respect and loyalty."

Edward turned to Richard. "Exactly, and so long as Henry lives, ambitious men will be tempted to use him to promote their own agenda."

The debate continued into the evening. Edward wavered, "If we allow him to live, we cannot keep him locked away in the White Tower."

Rivers attempted to save the old King. "He is harmless. Even his supporters concede that the country needs a ruler not a monk."

Edward wiped his brow and lowered his head. "I owe him a debt of gratitude for the benevolence he granted my Queen and young son."

Hastings interjected, "England will not see prosperity so long as war continues."

"My lords, we keep returning to the same solution!" Edward hesitated! "Henry will be martyred so that England may find peace." Solemnly, Edward signed the order and handed it to the Constable of England. "Richard, take this execution order and these noblemen with you to the Constable of the Tower, before I change my mind. Tell him that these orders are to be carried out immediately. He will know what to do."

It was coming on midnight when the Constable of the Tower read the order by torchlight. He motioned to a Yeoman, "Fetch an executioner!" Then he returned his attention to the group of lords, "Follow me!" Taciturn, the group climbed the stairs to Henry's cell. Reaching for his circular iron keychain, he fingered through the keys until he found the right one. Unlocking the door, he opened it to find Henry sitting with his head cocked to the side, carrying on a nonsensical conversation with an unseen visitor. "'Tis just as well! The old King's mind is muddled this evening! He doesn't know where he is. He won't be feeling anything!" John Howard reached for money to pay the executioner his fee.

The following evening, a guard of honor bore Henry VI's remains by torchlight to St. Paul's Cathedral where the body was laid out in state. Henry's head was uncovered discretely in such a way that all might see that Henry VI was dead. Though his heart had long stopped beating, his body spilled blood onto the pavement. When the corpse was escorted to Black Friars, the body bled anew. Blood trickled onto the floor. The doctors had no explanation. At last, the remains reached Chersey Abbey, where he was entombed. It was not long after his funeral that subjects, who remembered the benevolent king, began visiting Henry VI's crypt. It was said by some that miracles occurred for those who prayed at his sepulcher, and that the Pope should declare Henry VI a saint. Outside of violence, Edward did his best to suppress the growing cult.

The King's Man!

Now is the winter of our discontent
Made glorious summer by this son of York,
And all the clouds that loured upon our house
In the deep bosom of the ocean buried.
Now are our brows bound with victorious wreaths,
Our bruised arms hung up for monuments,
Our stern alarms changed to merry meetings,
Our dreadful marches to delightful measures.
Grim-visaged war hath smoothed his wrinkled front;
And now, instead of mounting barbed steeds
To fright the souls of fearful adversaries,
He capers nimbly in a lady's chamber
To the lascivious pleasing of a lute.

William Shakespeare

All of Edward IV's enemies were under lock and key, exiled or dead. Fourteen-year-old Henry Tudor and his uncle, Jasper Tudor, sailed for asylum in France. They were, however, betrayed and put ashore in Brittany. Both Louis XI and Edward IV made a request to Duke Francis for custody of the pair. Louis XI saw the Lancastrians as a way to keep the English King occupied and out of France. Edward IV viewed the Tudors as loose ends. Duke Francis was unwilling to relinquish such valuable political pawns. Francis only promised both kings that he would keep the Tudors under surveillance and provided for.

The Lancastrian cause, like a beached whale, seemed to be sputtering its last breath. With no one was left in England to challenge Edward's authority, he was able to put into play his father's dream. The York promise of reforms in government, law and finances were Edward's first priority. His second priority was to help the English merchants by recommencing treaty and trade agreements with Brittany, Burgundy and Castile.

131

Richard thought of Anne Neville as he assisted Edward with the organization of a new government, and again when he was preparing to head north. Abandoning all tasks for the moment, he traveled by barge and then carriage to visit Anne at the townhouse of George, Duke of Clarence. Warmly received, Richard was directed to the pretty, petite and thoroughly puzzled Anne. When they were left alone Anne bemoaned her fate, "I am now the landless daughter of a dead rebel." She almost asked Richard about her father and uncle, but had second thoughts. Richard had been like a family member, whom she respected and held in high regard. George was her brother-in-law. However, the Yorks had killed her father and uncle. Nothing would bring those she loved back to her! Powerless and perplexed, she was unable to cry!

The Crown had confiscated Warwick's estates. The Duke of Clarence laid claim to the estates of his mother-in-law, who was detained in the sanctuary of Beaulieu Abbey. Richard listened to Anne's story, took pity and comforted her. He had a debt of honor to repay the Nevilles. "I will speak with Edward." Demurely, Anne smiled.

It was essential that Edward have a man in the North whose loyalty was beyond question. Richard's offices of Chief Justice and Chamberlain of South Wales were transferred to the young Earl of Pembroke. Richard was to focus on the North and Scotland. Edward made Richard the Warden of the East and Middle Marches. He was granted Warwick's holdings in Yorkshire and Cumberland, which included the castles of Middleham, Penrith and Sheriff Hutton. Before leaving London, the King gave Richard permission to marry Anne Neville.

By the end of September, Richard had subdued the Scots, renegotiated a peace with James III and was back in London. When he returned to George's London home, his brother angrily confronted

Richard, "Neville family concerns are wholly in my hands!" Before Richard could protest, Clarence added, "Stay away from Anne Neville! She is not right for you!"

Dismayed and disgruntled, but not wishing to argue with his brother, Richard departed quietly and went to Edward for his advice. "The Duke of Clarence holds no legal right of wardship over Anne. I will draw up the order. Take Yeomen from my personal guard and deliver it to George."

The third time Richard appeared at his brother's door, George arrogantly read the order. Looking down at Richard, he bluntly stated, "She's not here! As I am not the one responsible for her whereabouts, I neither know nor care where she is."

Richard motioned to the Yeomen, "Search the entire home."

George had been forewarned. Confidently, he sat back to watch. "If anything is missing I'll be sending a bill to Edward."

Troubled by his brother's comments, Richard shrugged them off, setting about to assist the guards. A clandestine figure followed him. It was when he was on the second floor and alone that one of Anne's ladies touched Richard gently on his left upper arm. She gestured for him to follow her. In a quiet, dark corner, she looked around to make certain that they were not being overheard. She whispered, "Anne is at the home of John Smith, the Duke of Clarence's friend."

Richard returned to the carriage. With the Yeomen he set he off in search of Anne. Smith was taken a back when his servants informed him that the Duke of Gloucester and a company of the King's guard were awaiting him. This he had not expected; however, he would keep his promise to George! In their search of the home, Richard found Anne in the kitchen dressed as a maid. Escorting her out to his awaiting carriage, he took her to the sanctuary of St. Martin le Grand. She would be protected, yet under no obligation anyone.

The entire situation frustrated Edward to no end. He had better things to do! It wasn't until February that Edward was able to wrestle out a compromise that would satisfy the increasingly irascible George. George was made Constable of England and Richard was appointed to the lesser office of Warden of the Royal Forests beyond Trent. George was given the earldoms of Warwick and Salisbury as well as the majority of Warwick's estates. This included his mother-in-law's estates. With the other grants Edward had given him, the Duke of Clarence was the wealthiest man in the realm. Richard retained Middleham along with other castles, which Edward had already bestowed upon him. While hardly a pauper, Richard gave up a great deal to marry Anne. Begrudgingly, George stepped out of Richard's way!

When word was brought to Anne that Richard was waiting for her outside the abbey, she rushed out to greet him. The world was returning to her comprehension of it. Richard asked a good friar of St. Martin le Grand to marry them. They left for Middleham.

By early summer, Richard and Anne created a home. The Duchess of Gloucester presided over the communal routine of the Great Hall. She planned menus with her Steward of the Household, who supervised the carrying out of activities. He saw to it that his staff was clean and orderly. Utensils and plates were cleaned and polished, fresh cloths replaced soiled ones, and the tables were then properly set. He made certain that proprietary conduct was observed at all times. Etiquette was observed in the service of food and drink. Ale was the common drink; however, everyone had their choice of ale or watered wine. The Steward of the Household observed the carving of meat, making sure that sauces and soups were smooth, not lumpy.

At communal meals, Richard and Anne sat at the head table. Everyone else sat at tables down from them according to their station. When Richard took a pinch of salt from his saltcellar, the meal commenced. For each course, Richard was offered his choice of dishes. Before he ate, a servant tasted it.

Music was played throughout dinner. For feasts, short theatrical sketches were acted out while tablecloths were being changed for the next course. Into the alms baskets were placed leftovers for menial workers and beggars. The last course of a banquet was typically a large, carefully sculptured sugar or pastry model of something quite elegant, such as a swan. After being paraded through the Great Hall, it was then presented to Richard, at the head table, where it was dished out. Richard cared little for sweets and still had a good set of straight teeth.

Feasts were hallmarked by splendid entertainment, which followed the last course. Anne consulted beforehand with the Steward of the Household as to whether their own troupe or traveling players would be asked to perform. She questioned what the tumblers and mummers, who acted in verse, might do to entertain their guests. She fingered down the guest list so as to determine who might be called upon to sing or play an instrument. She worked with the Steward of the Household to roughly draft ideas for costumes that members of the household would wear, and how the portable stage might be decorated.

During the dancing, disguisers hastily burst into the Great Hall wearing fanciful attire, ornate headgear and masks. They would join in the dancing by selecting a partner from amongst the guests. As quickly as they entered, they departed;

leaving everyone to marvel at the costumes and wonder whom the masked individuals might be.

Richard's first priority was to replace lawlessness by dispensing justice. Lower gentry and peasants found relief from greedy landlords when they appealed to Richard's council. The Duke of Gloucester fairly arbitrated disagreements between principalities and individuals, regardless of class. He won the hearts and minds of the Northerners through aid. He funded such projects, such as repairing the Holy Trinity Priory in York. Richard enabled Northerners to be prosperous through such ventures as securing a license for the city of York to hold two fairs a year.

Richard took care to avoid offending Henry Percy, Earl of Northumberland, by including Percy in the affairs of the North. While Richard had authority over Cumberland and Westmorland, Percy's domain was the county of Northumberland. Both had commissions for Yorkshire, with Richard having the final word for West Riding and Percy for East Riding. Richard made Percy co-arbitrator in disputes among the gentry. He made it clear that the city of York was to consult the Earl and keep him advised. Northumberland was Richard's second in command.

York owed its prosperity to its location at the mouth of the river Ouse, whereby goods traveled to the Continent and on to the Baltic Sea. York was second only to London. In 1472, York's splendid Minster was completed. The cathedral along with numerous churches, the Abbey of St. Mary's, Holy Trinity Priory and the friaries of the four orders provided for men's souls. St. Leonard's Hospital and fifteen smaller hospitals dispensed medical care. Guildhall and the halls of the Merchant Adventures and Merchant Taylors provided space for trade union meetings, as well as city government. Both Richard and Miles Metcalfe were elected officers of the municipality. Sheriff Hutton was closest to Henry Percy and the city of York, but when Richard journeyed into York, he stayed with the Augustinian friars in Lendal.

Richard deliberated on an emblem for his banner. He wanted an insignia that was distinctive. The lesson of Montagu mistaking Oxford's radiating star for the York's great sun still played in his mind. At the same time, he wanted something uncomplicated. Mulling over the possibilities, he fell asleep. He was groggy when he awoke the following morning, but clearly in his mind he saw a white boar. He awakened fully, considering the option — when cornered a wild boar fights ferociously. It fit! It was perfect!

His motto came to him more easily. 'Loyalty binds me' expressed his adherence and support for King Edward. It also adequately described the life Richard had chosen for himself.

London was a five to six-day journey from Middleham, depending upon how hard one was willing to ride. Richard made the journey whenever he was called to court to attend affairs of state and by his duty to the King. In the fall, Richard left Anne, who was pregnant, in Wensleydale while he rode to London to attend Parliament.

1473 was the year Sixtus IV, the first pope to authorize the selling of indulgences for the dead, built the Sistine Chapel. In that same year, Edward IV sent his son, Edward, to Ludlow Castle, away from courtly intrigues and the dangers of contracting the plague. Prince Edward was to be raised under the direct supervision of Anthony Woodville, Earl Rivers, who was different from his family, but a Woodville nonetheless.

It was also in I473, that Anne Neville gave birth to a son. The baby's parents named him Edward, after his illustrious uncle. Richard's two illegitimate children had been born healthy and were growing up strong. However, the bloodlines between Anne and Richard were thin, too thin! Edward was not robust, but he lived!

In May, Richard met with Henry Percy, Earl of Northumberland, and Edward IV at Nottingham. The purpose was to firm up an agreeable working relationship in the North. Northumberland was genial. In the back of his mind, Richard knew that John Neville would have been more dependable. He said nothing to Edward!

Anne was become increasingly concerned for the welfare of her mother. Richard found the opportunity at Nottingham to ask Edward to release the Countess of Warwick to him. Edward agreed! The petulant Duke of Clarence was ardently opposed! When Anne's mother was asked if she wished to join the Duke of Gloucester's household, the Countess heartily consented. However, her position in society as the wife of a dead traitor was not the same as the Dowager Duchess of York.

George was infuriated! He turned to his old comrade, George Neville, the Archbishop of York, whom Edward had pardoned and released at the request of Richard. The ungrateful Archbishop no sooner had been released, than he contacted John de Vere, Earl of Oxford. With Louis XI's assistance, Oxford was supervising raids on Calais. Edward's spies discovered the conspiracy and informed the King. The Archbishop was promptly re-arrested! It was out of Richard's hands!

George then turned to Oxford, who had lost a father and a brother to the Lancastrian cause. The ever-scheming Louis XI seized the opportunity to complicate Edward's life by conspiring with them both. Louis reasoned that if Edward was busy with interesting matters at home, his attention would be divert away from France.

While Henry VI was able to inspire the hearts of many Englanders, the Lancastrian cause per say did not. Oxford received a chilly welcome when his fleet landed on English shores. Discovering that Essex, Duras and Dynham were on their way to engaging him in combat, Oxford took to the seas. Turning to piracy, Oxford took what merchant ships he was able to confiscate.

In September, Edward issued a commission of array to Richard, who promptly marched south with his Yorkshire men to take on Oxford. George used the opportunity to muster men so that he might avenge himself against Gloucester. The Duke of Clarence's real motive, to seize the crown, was transparent to everyone.

Louis dared not risk open warfare with England. After surmising that Oxford and Clarence had little chance of overthrowing Edward, Louis sent no support. By February 1474, Oxford surrendered, walking away with only his life. Subdued, Clarence was forced to appeal to Edward so that he might retain his property.

Boldly, and with acrid antagonism, Clarence wanted the issue of Warwick's estates to be reopened. Edward groaned at the prospect of bargaining back and forth with George! Richard agreed to the negotiations, hoping to bring about family peace. Queen Elizabeth could hardly believe the Duke of Clarence was being let off again! She was not alone! Instead of having his property confiscated George would end up with more.

As if Warwick's widow were in her grave, her estates were divided up equally and given, not to Richard and George, but to Anne and Isabel. Edward went a step further and granted Clarence other estates. Edward, himself, held out the deeds for George to take. Clarence, smiling overconfidently, reached out for the rolled parchments, but Edward did not relinquish his hold immediately. Rather, he held on for a moment. Looking Clarence in the eye, Edward said, "Let this be the end of it, George!"

In the spring of 1475, Edward felt he was in a position to begin preparations for war against France. His subjects expected it! For the cause, Parliament conferred large grants, magnates bestowed hefty sums and the Duke of Burgundy agreed to bring an army.

Each English lord entered into a contract with the King to supply men-at-arms and archers, who were paid for their services. Each soldier wore the badge of the nobleman he fought under. More than double the number of Yorkshire men that Richard had pledged to Edward, assembled under Richard's white boar.

Richard had succeeded in winning the hearts of the Yorkshire men. He possessed superb generalship abilities. He kept peace in the Marches. His private life and public activities were exemplary. Edward was thrilled at the size of Richard's army; he rewarded Richard by granting him the enormous York fortress of Skipton. In addition, he expanded the Duke of Gloucester's authority as Sheriff of Cumberland.

On July 4th, the Plantagenets joined the gathering forces in Calais. Margaret, Duchess of Burgundy, arrived two days later, to welcome her three brothers. She was particularly delighted to see George, who had always been her favorite. Afterwards, Edward organized and provided for the troops. George and Richard returned with Margaret and her stepdaughter, the beautiful Mary of Burgundy, to St. Omer. The exquisitely opulent estate was a mirror of Burgundy's wealth.

George was at his best, being quite taken by Mary. For her part, she was flattered, taking pleasure in his obsequious manners and witty humor. The days passed in easy comfort while they waited for Margaret's husband to return.

Not for nothing was the Duke of Burgundy called Charles the Rash! His short temper once again replaced his thinking. Charles had taken his entire army to the east to put down a minor

140

squabble. When he showed up in Calais with only a bodyguard on July 14, Edward viewed it as a decisive blow! Edward conferred with his commanders. They agreed to proceed with caution.

Louis XI was approaching Calais with a sizeable army. Edward weighed his options. He was running out of money! However, English archers were unequalled! His forces might easily win the war. However, without the Duke of Burgundy's army Edward would not secure a decisive victory. Thus, the costs of maintaining control in France would be exorbitant.

Edward sent out a feeler, to see if Louis XI would negotiate for peace. France needed time that peace afforded to become a strong nation-state. While ambassadors were dispatched, Edward consulted with his royal captains. Richard of Gloucester was among the very few who favored continuance of the campaign.

In return for England's immediate withdrawal and a seven-year truce, Louis XI agreed to pay Edward 75,000 gold crowns immediately and 50,000 crowns a year. The Dauphin was to marry Princess Elizabeth. Trade agreements were established between the two countries. 50,000 additional crowns were paid to Edward for the release of Queen Margaret. By accepting Louis' offer, Edward's subjects would not be burdened with the enormous expenditures of maintaining a partial conquest of France. Edward's annuity would give him self-sufficiency; he would not have to go to Parliament for grants or the people for taxes.

When Charles of Burgundy learned of the agreement, he scathingly rebuked Edward. Edward was unmoved! For his sister's sake Edward restrained himself, maintaining his composure.

Louis rolled out the red carpet. The festivities surrounding the peace accord were fabulous. With Edward's blessing, Louis used the festivities to win over as many English lords as possible with pensions and gifts. Edward made a grand appearance dressed to the nines. Much like Henry VI, Louis cared little for cloth of gold or expensive jewels. Louis showed up at the ceremony in comfortable garb. Richard neither dressed for nor attended the signing of the treaty.

Louis was unwilling to give up on the English Prince. After the signing, Louis invited the Duke of Gloucester to dinner. He presented Richard with gifts of plate and magnificent horses. Richard only accepted the presents after he was assured that they were not a bribe. Though Louis did his best, Richard remained unenthusiastic for the French cause. At the end of the day, Louis marked Richard as an enemy of France.

Edward never held a man accountable whose opinion differed from his own - on the contrary, he welcomed diverse thoughts. What changed when Edward did not conquer France was that his shining star lost a bit of its luster in the eyes of Richard and his subjects. However, everyone knew that Richard, Duke of Gloucester, had stood firm for English claims to French territory.

Disbanded soldiers returned to England without spoils or grandeur. Some turned to highway robbery. Outlaws lurked in the forests, ready to rob travelers, murdering those who resisted. Edward responded with zeal. He sought out the criminals; his judges dispensed justice with equality. Anyone, regardless of his or her position, who was found guilty of homicide or thievery, was hanged. When order was restored, Edward IV's tarnished star seemed a tad refurbished. But Englanders looked for a scapegoat for what they perceived of as English relenting to French demands. They held those responsible who had advised Edward, to accept the French King's treaty.

Edward turned to adulterous liaisons more and more, going through women, married and unmarried, noble and common, like an army that had outflanked the opposition and was rolling up the line. He never forced a woman to his bed. Instead, he made promises and gave gifts. Quickly having his fill, he cast them aside like yesterday's laundry. Edward's three constant companions in debauchery were his two stepsons and one of the Queen's brothers. Lord Hastings, the harbinger of Court intrigue, could be counted upon for a go at it as well. The goings-on in the English pleasure palace were the gossip of Continental Europe.

However, something changed when Edward returned to London. Jane Shore, the wife of a London merchant, won his heart. He visited his wife's chambers infrequently. Of all Edward's mistresses, Queen Elizabeth resented the lovely Jane Shore most of all. However, the King did not give up other women immediately for Jane, whom he referred to as the merriest woman in the entire realm. Both Hastings and the Marquess of Dorset, who hated one another and competed for the position as the King's main man, loved Jane as well. Each hoped that Edward would tire of her and cast her aside as he had done with the others.

Richard found court intrigue tiresome. He was glad to head home! Upon returning to Middleham, he was informed that there was a problem with the fish traps. Fish traps consisted of a system of nets and wicker 'rooms'. Magnates, abbots and bishops set them up in rivers to catch fish in vast numbers so that they could feed their large households. Commoners detested fish traps, which hindered river traffic and limited the number of available fish that could be caught by hook and line. The government of York had been given permission in 1463 to supervise the placement of fish traps and to remove illegal ones. However, powerful interests often skirted the law. To solve the problem, Parliament had just strengthened the city of York's authority in the matter.

City fathers showed this commission to the Duke of Gloucester and asked for his help. Richard dictated letters to his secretary, John Kendall, who sent them out to Richard's bailiffs and tenants, asking them to remove the fish traps. When the Bishop of Durham asked the Duke of Gloucester why he bothered with such a trivial matter, Richard responded, "Because it is important to people whose bellies are not full." Richard's kindness extended to others as well. When Edward withdrew the dukedom from Montegu's son, Richard took the boy into his household.

Wishing to draw attention away from France, in July 1476, Edward IV had the bodies of his father and brother exhumed from their plain tombs at Pontefract. The remains traveled for one week under royal escort to Fotheringhay. Funerals, especially royal funerals, were usually quiet affairs conducted at night. Edward threw custom aside! Edward and several of his advisors planned with scrutinizing detail, a solemn celebration and royal ceremony, which rivaled a coronation. Nobility and officers of the City of York attended the high mass. With all dignity and honor, the remains of the dukes of York and Rutland were placed in a vault beneath the church. Edward and Richard served dinner to more than 2,000 individuals. Trumpets and clarions heralded courses of meat and fowl, sweets and wine. Musicians played throughout the feast; plays were performed afterwards. Edward and Richard gave alms to over 5,000 people.

The Man Who Would Be King

He hearkens after prophecies and dreams,
And from the crossrow plucks the letter G,
And says a wizard told him that by "G"
His issue disinherited should be.
And for my name of George begins with G,
It follows in his thought that I am he.
These, as I learn, and such like toys as these
Hath moved his Highness to commit me now.

William Shakespeare

On December 22, 1476, Isabel, the Duchess of Clarence, died in childbirth; her son survived for only a few days. On January 5th, 1477, Charles the Rash of Burgundy died. Overnight, his daughter, Mary, became the supreme heiress in all of Europe. Quick to respond, Louis XI arrayed his army, audaciously asserting France's claim to the Duchy of Burgundy. In haste, Edward IV called his council. However, Edward hesitated to attack Louis XI. If he pursued a coarse of war against France, he would lose his yearly stipend. English envoys and messengers were dispatched to Margaret, Dowager Duchess of Burgundy, Mary of Burgundy and Louis XI.

Margaret offered a solution; her cherished brother, George, should wed Mary. Fearing that the Duke of Clarence would use Burgundy's vast resources to claim the English throne as well, Edward refused the offer. Mary declined as well. She had fallen in love with a man whom she thought would save her realm. Before his death, Charles had signed an agreement by which Mary was betrothed to Maximilian, the handsome, chivalrous, only son of Frederick III, Duke of Austria and Holy Roman Emperor.

George had no ear to hear Mary's refusal, or face the fact that her father had already signed a contract of marriage. All George focused on was

Edward's interference! As if matters were not bad enough, under the urging of Queen Elizabeth, Edward proposed Anthony, Earl Rivers, as a potential groom for Mary. Mary refused Anthony more emphatically than she had George. George had not the eyes to see that his brother had offered the proposal to satisfy his wife. Instead, he acrimoniously chewed over his loss and grumbled through court. Sympathy was building for George. However, when it was discovered that he was extorting money from Lord Dynham, empathy for George's cause ended.

In April, George took upon himself the role of king. He seized, tried and executed two individuals whom he falsely charged with poisoning his wife and infant son. The underlying implication was that the executed had carried out the deed for the Woodvilles and Edward IV.

Edward responded with a warning to George. A member of George's household was arrested, tried and executed on charges of distributing treasonous documents and plotting the King's death through magic. George retaliated by impudently barging in on the King, interrupting his Council meeting. To a man, Edward's Council wondered, when would the King put an end to his brother's dodgy, imprudent behavior? Queen Elizabeth threw her hands up in dismay! Edward only reproached George!

Undaunted by Edward's reprimand, George followed up his actions by rekindling and spreading the old gossip that Edward was a bastard. George also included unbelievable, reckless claims against the King. Thus, not much heed was given to assertions of Edward's illegitimacy. Most people assumed that the Duke of Clarence was saying anything just to be king. Richard worried over George's rash behavior.

In late spring of 1477, Anne convinced Richard that as friends of the city, they were expected to be in York for the festival of Corpus Christie. "It will keep your mind off of your family's squabbles. You may just enjoy yourself."

"You are right!"

After Richard sent his acknowledgement to the officers of the city, an invitation was extended back. The Duke and Duchess of Gloucester were asked to become members of the Corpus Christi Guild. The Duchess of York had been inducted twenty-one years earlier. Richard wrote to his mother to tell her.

Cecily answered back, "The induction into the Guild is an honor bestowed upon those whom the city favors. I am proud of you and know that your father would be well pleased with your efforts. I am planning on being in York for the occasion!"

York was famous for Mystery plays, which were short scenes based on stories from the Bible. Over five hundred male members of the city's guilds performed them. Fifty or so sacred plays were presented throughout the day; performances began at dawn. The Miracle Plays were extremely popular and so well attended that they had long since outgrown the space available in churches.

Wagons paraded through the city carrying actors, props and scenery to designated sites. Wealthy men paid for the privilege of having performances in their private courtyards or halls. Though the plays were religious, they could also be comical or risky. For special effects in the nativity scene, two men under a donkey skin pushed manure out onto the stage from under the tail. John the Baptist laid prone waiting for his head to be chopped off. Only at the last moment was a dummy substituted for the actor. When the Baptist's mock-up head was severed, the axe split open a bag of pig's blood. Blood spattered across the stage and oftentimes, onto the audience. The finale included Judas hanging himself.

The evening following Corpus Christie, Richard and Anne were escorted by torch and candlelight in a stately procession from the Holy Trinity Priory to the Minster. Flowers, crosses, banners and pennons delineated the path. Flower petals were strewn before them. Guild members and city officers followed the couple. Four strong men carried an elaborate silver shrine containing a beryl vase, housing the sacred elements. The high platform moved slowly through the city. Richard's heart gladdened at the esteem and love the citizens of York showed him. He wished his father were alive to witness his moment of accomplishment. But more so, to settle the matter between his brothers! The Duke of York would never have allowed his son's dispute to escalate to its present level of outright antagonism.

Always ready and available to make Edward's life complicated, in June, Louis XI sent word to the English King. The message stated, "My dearest friend, Edward, my spies have brought me information of calamitous proportions. It is my duty as your friend to bring this news to your attention. I have learned from reliable sources that the motive behind your brother, George, Duke of Clarence, wanting to wed Mary of Burgundy was to sequester the English crown from you."

What tipped the scales was not Louis' questionably thoughtful proclamation, but rather news from one of Edward's spies. George, Duke of Clarence, had told several people that Edward IV's children were bastards. The whole lot of princes and princesses were illegitimate because the King was already married to Lady Eleanor Butler when he married Elizabeth Woodville.

Edward IV ordered George's arrest! The following day, George dissembled politely in front of Edward under the escort of two Yeomen. Edward briskly ordered his men, "Yeoman allow my brother to approach me unescorted." Guards stepped aside. George, not quite as carefree as usual, walked up to his brother. Edward spoke first, but in muted tones so that the men near the door would be unable to bare witness. "I am having you arrested on charges of treason!"

George half smiled and spoke under his breath, "I will expose you and your children as bastards!"

Edward's lips pressed tightly together; his jaw set in an unfamiliar gesture. Quietly, but firmly Edward responded, "You have just played that card and no one believes you."

"It does not change the fact that you and your children are bastards. I am the rightful heir to the throne!"

Edward winced, "Through our mother Edward III's blood flows through my veins! Through my generalship, my leadership, my popularity the kingdom is at peace and prospers. Through my generosity you have been elevated in prominence, position and possessions. Why was that not enough for you? By what ungodly mandate, have you justified blackmailing your own kin?" Softening, Edward added, "My responsibility is that I should never have given in to your demands."

Edward called the Lord Mayor of London, who was standing at a distance near the door with the guards. "Take what Yeomen you require and escort George, Duke of Clarence, to the White Tower." Edward sighed in relief, as he watched George being taken away; his eyes riveted on his George's back. Edward saw not his brother, but the millstone of his personal angst leaving the chamber. What had plagued him for too many years would soon be ended.

The following day, Stillington, Bishop of Bath and Wells, was summoned to the King's presence. The Bishop entered Edward's apartments to be greeted by an out-of-character, stern-faced

King. The Bishop bowed, "What pleases my sovereign?"

"George, Duke of Clarence, has been spreading rumors that there was a precontract of marriage between myself and Lady Eleanor at the time I married Elizabeth Woodville. Therefore, my children are bastards." The Bishop nervously fidgeted. Edward continued, "There is only one person he could have heard that from." Stillington looked up as Edward said, "You!"

"My King . . ."

Edward interrupted! He had no patience for excuses. "Your words are treasonous and threaten the stability of the realm." Droplets of sweat formed beads on the Bishop's brow. Edward knew that his point had hit its target. "I am inclined to grant mercy under the condition that you swear an oath of silence on this matter!"

"Of course, my Liege!"

"In addition, you are to be fined heavily and secured in the White Tower for several months." Under the circumstances, Stillington breathed a slight sigh.

Richard set out for London as soon as he learned of George's fate. Edward received Richard in private. Edward was curious to know if George had shared his information with Richard. Richard entered the room with pleading eyes. "Edward, I am your man forever!" Richard dropped to his knees. "You have pardoned others, including George, for crimes of larger magnitude. Please extend your mercy to our brother!"

Edward listened with compassion and while he longed to tell Richard of George's real crime, he knew that was not possible. He had considered his words carefully before Richard's expected arrival. On the one hand, Edward was determined to put an end to the incessant blackmail. He had given up on George's promises. On the other hand, Edward did not want to lose Richard's love or respect.

Richard was the prop to his throne! Edward offered reasoning, "There is no end to George's plotting. The next debacle may very well be more than a farce. More people may die."

"With all deference, may I be so bold as to assert that you speak in hyperboles. With Oxford out of the way, George will find no cohort to support his schemes."

Edward stood up and in his manner, grasped a hold of Richard's upper arms and shoulders. "At one time, George was the wealthiest noble in the realm. Yet, that failed to satisfy him. Why would England's scepter gratify him? George is unable to find happiness in this world. Perhaps, he will find it in the next."

Christmas season was a lively affair. William Caxton's printing company, the Red Pale, had been established the year before. They had just published *The Dictes and Sayings of the Philosophers,* which had been translated from French to English by the well-traveled Anthony, Earl Rivers. Anthony Woodville was a different cut from the rest of his family. His nature sported contradictions. He was Europe's foremost jouster, but he had never distinguished himself in battle. He considered himself a devout Catholic, but he had mystical experiences. He wore the latest fashions, but underneath he wore a hair shirt that he might do penance.

Christmas found Queen Elizabeth elatedly gliding through palace corridors wearing a continuous smile. No Hottentot, backwoods Northerner would underhandedly seize her moment of revenge for her father's death! Gaily, she busied herself with final preparations for her youngest son's precontract in marriage to the six-year-old heiress of the house of Norfolk.

On January 15, 1478, all of the nobility in the land, with the exception of the Duke of Clarence, gathered for the formal wedding of four-year-old Prince Richard. Richard, Duke of Gloucester, was physically present; his mind was preoccupied with George. Though troubled, Richard joined in the festivities. It was where he would find Edward.

Richard was only slightly above average in height. Next to Edward, everyone but Hastings appeared small in stature. Richard had a cordial nature and was sought out during the festivities. After the Countess of Desmond finished dancing with Richard, she commented, "Richard of Gloucester is the handsomest man in the room with the exception of his brother, King Edward."

At times, Richard felt that his pleas touched cords of mercy within the arbiter of George's fate. Or perhaps, the decorous Dowager Duchess of York had appealed to Edward's family responsibilities. Then, as if Queen Elizabeth had gone into throes of emotional outcries, Edward became impenetrable; nay, resolute that George must answer for his treachery.

Others besides Richard and George did not celebrated the opening of the New Year. Pope Sixtus IV gave permission for the Spanish sovereigns to set up the Holy Inquisition. Thus far, Edward had managed to keep peace with the Pope and the Inquisition out of England.

Richard attempted again to appeal for George's release before the Twelfth Night, but it was to no avail. When the boar's head was ceremoniously brought out, George was still under lock and key in the White Tower. George was beginning to worry, but then there was Richard.

Edward pressed forward with his plans to have George declared a traitor. He gathered peers to sit in judgment of the wayward prince. The evidence against George, Duke of Clarence, was clear. On February 7th, the Duke of Buckingham, Steward of England, found Clarence guilty of high treason. Though relief was in sight for the King, Edward hesitated to sign the execution order for ten days. Richard saw Edward's dithering as an opportunity to supplicate on George's behalf. At the same time, the Queen pressed unmercifully for George's execution. Each one was fully aware that the other was pleading a contrary cause.

The King was not given to superstition; after all, the Catholic Church did not believe in ghosts. Elizabeth played her mystic card just the same. She was undaunted; George was too near her grasp to let go now. "Edward, have you not forgotten the sage, who prophesized that a man whose name begins with the letter 'G' will disinherit your sons? Would you deny the Prince of Wales the throne? George must go!"

At the end of the day, it was Edward's weariness of being blackmailed that caused him to sign George's execution order. On February 18th, George was informed that he was to be executed and asked if he had a last request. In a last attempt at humor and theatrics he replied. "Ask the King to bring two barrels of wine. When I and my friends are thoroughly drunk on the first, Edward may have me drowned me in the second."

After hearing his brother's last request, Edward reluctantly agreed. "Hastings, let's keep this drama as quiet as possible!" Edward added, "Let the guards bring Malmsey wine. Perhaps, the Duke of Clarence will be reminded of my past generosity."

Lord Hastings inquired only half in jest, "Will they be serving food in the Tower as well?"

While the Duke of Clarence's closest friends were planning to be with George at his farewell bash, the Duke of Gloucester could not bare to attend. Instead, he deliberately made his way to his brother's cell the day before. George, resigned to his fate, smiled sheepishly when

Richard entered his cell. "You were always my favorite brother, Richard!"

"I was the only brother you knew!"

That wasn't quite right! George knew Edward well. It was George's envy that colored him a murky pea green. The Duke of Clarence had nurtured his dream of becoming king for so long that even now, those desires crept into his consciousness. "Edward's right, you know! I did yearn to be king." George smiled, "I would have been good at it, you know!" George faltered, "You aren't coming tomorrow, are you?"

Unexpected tears flooded Richard's eyes and streamed down his face. Overwhelmed with emotion, he was unable to lift his hand to wipe them away. "I could not stand by and do nothing."

The smile was erased from George's face for the moment. He had never discussed with Richard the fact that Edward had been a bastard. Better to have let the old Earl of Warwick be the bearer of ill tidings. Assessing the situation at hand, George made the decision not to dwell on Edward's or the princes' origins. He let it go! Besides, Richard might put two and two together and figure out that he, the brother Richard had looked up to, had been blackmailing the king. At this particular moment, the prospect of Richard's prayers provided some measure of comfort. "Is mother coming?"

"She'll be up to see you shortly."

Richard departed, his heart filled with sorrow. As had been prearranged by Edward, the Yeoman on guard duty sought out the King. He reported George and Richard's conversation. Edward was well pleased. Edward knew that in spite of everything, Richard was still his man.

The party was limited to only a select few of George's friends, who had been strictly instructed by the King's men to say nothing of the manner of the Duke of Clarence's demise. George's friends drank sparingly. Doing the best they could, they tried to keep a light, easy manner. However, the presence of the executioner kept George's mind thinking and conscious. When at last he passed out, George was drowned in the wine.

At first, George did not realize that he was dead. The wine had had a woozy effect on his spirit. His form was much like that of his physical body! He spoke to his friends, but they acted as if they neither saw nor heard him. He was confused! It was the wine. He turned to see the vestiges of his physical body, like worn clothes, heaped on the floor. The lid with which George had furtively kept his guilt and anger buried with in life was gone! Heavy emotions he carried in life now weighed him down. The Light, the corridor to the next dimension, which is available to all souls of the departed, was out of reach, out of sight.

When his friends left the cell, George followed, finding it humorous as he passed by the guards undetected. Down the stairs, the party walked silently out onto the Tower Green. It was when they reached the cobblestone road leading to the bridge that George found himself unable to precede further. He had hoped to speak with Edward, but it would appear that his haunt was limited to the Tower of London.

After George's death, Richard was given Richmond Castle in exchange for three other manors that he held. He was also given back the title and responsibilities of the office of Constable of England, which he had relinquished to George some six years before. Edward sequestered Clarence's estates for the Crown. Clarence's son and heir would be named the Earl of Warwick when he came of age. George's daughter, Margaret, entered Edward's household.

Anguished with immeasurable sorrow, Richard headed to Middleham shortly after George's funeral. He did not speak on the journey home. His companions left him to his grieving. Richard, deep in thought, tried to reconcile a sense that had come, as quietly as a stalking cat, when he had gone to the White Tower to claim George's body. It was as if he could almost sense George's presence. Richard recalled the night in the Low Countries when his father's spirit had come to him, before departing in a burst of Light. Why was George's presence different from that of his father's? He did not know! Maybe his mind had played tricks on him? But then there was one of the guardsmen, who nervously but knowingly, noted Richard's reaction to the unseen but familiar pat on his shoulder.

Though the officers of Richard's household tried to shield him from mundane matters, a problem with the fish traps returned. Richard made his way to the Great Hall. Glancing at the men standing behind the guards with hat in hand, he gestured for them to step forward. He heard their complaint. Thrusting himself into resolving the problem, he found himself not thinking about George's death. Afterwards, Richard plunged deeply into his world. Oftentimes, he retreated for days into the silence and solitude of his mind. Routinely going about his tasks, he emerged from his private abyss somewhat lighter.

He would never forget George, but slowly throughout the year the emptiness of George's loss along with his own personal pain subsided. One day, he found himself smiling when he recalled George laughing at him in their mother's coach on the way to Ludlow Castle. It surprised him!

Richard secured the proper licenses and founded colleges at Barnard and Middleham. His only request was that the clerics pray for his family. Besides the Duke of Clarence, he included all of the King's living and diseased brothers and sisters, Edward and Elizabeth, Anne and himself, his children and all of his nieces and nephews.

Lord of the North

Richard came to court less often; when he did, he could hardly fail to notice that Edward was outgrowing his armor. Edward was not without feelings. While unapologetic for George's demise, he increasingly hid the ramifications and guilt of his first marriage in delights of fine cuisine, eloquent pastries and exceptional wines. He especially loved sweet-sour spiced rabbit that had been fried up in plenty of fat, Lombard chicken pasties with large thick slices of bacon, white breads and pastries, pork rolls, roast pheasant, broiled venison with pepper sauce, spit-roasted steaks, poached fowl cooked with bacon and served with pudding, and haddock in a tasty sauce. He enjoyed all desserts from fried fig pastries to cream custard tarts, rose pudding and especially cherry pottage with plenty of sugar, butter and breadcrumbs. Unlike his parents and siblings, Edward avoided at all cost green dishes, such as, cabbage chowder, golden leeks and onions, and even leeks and sops in wine.

Unable to either fully blame George or totally accept responsibility for the way in which events unfolded, Edward recalled most clearly Elizabeth's insistence that George must die. Like Salome dancing for the head of John the Baptist, Elizabeth had beseeched him to execute George. Edward buried his emotions under piles of food, following the Roman style of gorging. Richard failed to comprehend Edward's own role in his downward slide. Richard was only willing to see the Woodvilles as the thrust behind George's death and the corruptors of Edward IV.

The Court bubbled with intrigue, which Richard wanted no part of. A bitter feud between the Woodvilles and the older nobility had gotten entirely out of control and Edward refused to intervene. Lords, like Henry Stafford, Duke of Buckingham, who had been forced to marry sisters of the Queen, had never forgiven Elizabeth. The Woodvilles were seen to all, as insolent and ostentatious. The leader of the opposition to the Woodvilles was William Hastings, who was frequently the brunt of Woodville hostility, as he was the King's dearest friend. Dorset was in competition with Hastings to be Edward's chief companion and comrade in his licentious affairs. The Queen overlooked Dorset's role and the complicity of her brothers, Lionel and Edward, in her husband's wantonness. She blamed the King's depravity solely on Hastings. When Edward IV took the captaincy of Calais from Rivers and gave it to Hastings, Rivers blamed Hastings. Lords and ladies on both sides bought the services of servants, paying them to spy on one another and the King.

In the North, Richard had already made inroads into the hearts of Northerners by dispensing favors and establishing order. Richard, personally ambitious, also worked to increase his holdings and personal wealth. He established himself closer to York by trading some of his holdings for property around the city. In all of his dealings, however, he never compromised his values for business. It was one of the lessons that the remarkable Duke of York had instilled firmly into Richard's consciousness. "Remember the words of Jesus — how can we be trusted with the keys of heaven if we cannot be trusted with the meager things of earth?"

Richard administered impartial justice, sometimes finding against his own servants and friends. Thus, men and whole towns sought him out to settle their affairs. Through both his military acumen and his readiness to dispense mercy, Richard kept peace in the Marches. He was faithful to his wife and loved his son above all else. Thus, brick by brick Richard's personal reputation grew. By delegating the judicial work of his offices to other capable hands, Richard was left free to concentrate on his position as Warden of the West Marches, live the life of a country lord and enjoy his family.

Richard, however, had not found in Anne the intense love he and George had read about in books of romance and chivalry. There had never been passion to develop into deep love! He saw Anne as a friend. For her part, Anne had never come to terms with the manner of her father and uncle's death. He had married out of obligation, she as a matter of necessity. Their relations were polite.

If there was anything Richard envied Edward for, it was his brother's passionate love, first for Elizabeth Woodville and now for Jane Shore. He would never admit it, hiding his true feelings under a mantel of distain for Jane, Hastings and the Woodvilles. They were purveyors of degenerate behavior, causing his brother to stray. As for Edward, he had fallen into accepting a role of keeping order and maintaining the status quo.

Richard's five-year-old son, Edward, was not strong of body but his young heart had an immense capacity for love. A handsome boy with kind, blue eyes, he endeared himself to people. Edward's father was his biggest fan! Richard's heartfelt fatherly love nudged him back into life, making feel alive again. Slowly, the empty place in his chest healed. Whenever he was at Middleham, Richard made the time to see his son.

In the summer of 1480, Richard came to London to visit his sister, Margaret, Dowager Duchess of Burgundy. She had come to plead with Edward for the Burgundy cause. Her stepdaughter, Mary had married Maximillian, whose his father was still the German Emperor. Maximillian, while a superb general, had no money of his own. Louis was in the process of swallowing Burgundy. Unwilling to give up 50,000 gold pieces, which Louis paid him yearly, Edward did nothing.

Richard met Margaret at Baynard's Castle in London. Cecily, delighted to have her daughter at home, glowed. Richard thought it was the first time he had seen his mother happy since George had died. Margaret was still attractive, though worry lines creased her forehead and knitted her eyebrows together. Not wishing to upset her mother, only when they were alone did Margaret ask Richard about George. "Were you with George when he died? How was he?"

Richard offered words of comfort. "I saw him the day before." He hesitated, "I did my best to try to persuade Edward to spare his life."

Margaret broke down in tears. Richard put his arm around Margaret. "Poor George!"

"I miss him as well! Margaret, please do not blame Edward."

In a ploy to occupy Edward so that he could take Burgundy, Louis convinced James III of Scotland to conduct border raids. By the spring of 1980, the problem had escalated, forcing Edward to take action. Edward named Richard his Lieutenant General in the North. However, there were not enough men in the North to array an army large enough to invade Scotland. Edward's response was only defensive! Richard determined that if a raiding party moved quickly and with sufficient force, it might make the Scots pay heed. By September, Richard and his forces were ready. He led a brief, but effective campaign that halted Scottish forays. It gave Edward a victory he could take to Parliament.

In October, Richard was at Sheriff Hutton taking care of business in York. While Richard was in residence at Sheriff Hutton, the Earl of

160

Northumberland sent a written demand to the city of York. "I charge you to marshal enough men to provide a force ready to await my orders. This is to be done without delay or you will answer at your own peril."

Affronted at the Earl's attitude, a city minister was dispatched to Sheriff Hutton to consult with the Duke of Gloucester. Treading carefully, so as not to step on the Earl's toes, Richard first assured the city that the Scots were under control for the time being. He would speak with the Earl! When the officials left, Richard rode to Wressell to speak with Henry Percy, who knew nothing of Richard's intervention.

As soon as the sentry saw the approaching white boar banner of the Duke of Gloucester, word was sent to the Earl. Promptly, preparations were made to receive the Prince's small party. The guardsmen acknowledged Richard as he rode across the drawbridge and into the inner courtyard. Dismounting his white charger, Richard's men followed his lead. Smiling, he clasped the Earl warmly. While the horses were being stabled, the two magnets walked up the steps to the Great Hall, where tables were set and servers held dishes of food. "What brings you here, Richard?"

"My couriers have informed me that the Scottish incursions have ended. The threat is under control for now." Richard drank his wine. "Edward has sent word that he would like the two of us to concentrate on preparations for a crucial campaign that will be launched against Scotland in the coming summer."

"Did the King say what my role is to be?"

"You and your officers are to conduct a census to ascertain the number of men available for a military operation."

"And you?"

"I will be overseeing repairs to Carlisle Castle and recruiting men to reinforce garrisons along the boarder."

"I have just recently sent orders to York that they are to prepare troops now."

"As the Marches are secure, perhaps, it would be best to send word that their services are not needed for the moment, but that you will be making inquiries in preparation for an array of men to march in battle against the Scots."

The Earl appeared satisfied. He dispatched a courier. Yet, he was not entirely content.

Raising an army by indenture and sustaining it in the field required enormous funds. The Lords were unwilling to contribute significant amounts after the French debacle. Edward turned to Parliament to raise taxes - an unpopular measure! Richard talked Edward into exempting the city of York, because of their recent successful effort in Scotland. Instead, he promised 120 archers!

Lord Howard's fleet began the assault against Scotland in the summer of 1481. Intrepidly sailing into the Firth of Forth, he immobilized Scottish shipping and burned Blackness. Edward was to follow Howard with an army, joining up with Richard and Henry Percy in the North. However, Edward's health was failing. In addition, turmoil had been created by the Parliamentary tax. Edward was definitively prevented from leaving London.

With Northumberland as his second in command, Richard led his army of only a few thousand men into Scottish territory. James III had amassed a huge force. Quarreling Scottish barons, however, slowed the Scottish King. Richard's propensity for locating the enemy did not fail him. Assessing the situation, he struck quickly and decisively along the boarder. After each victory, Richard speedily refurbished and regrouped so as to encounter his adversary again.

The October harvest was scant in England and throughout Europe. December 1481 was particularly harsh. Many starved! Edward managed the journey

to Nottingham to discuss the problem and provide
Richard with funds. After consulting with Richard,
Edward laid out plans for a full military invasion
of Scotland.

The Queen was aware of her husband's ill
health. However, it was through one of her moles,
a young palace cook, when she had an inkling of
why. One day, the cook was sent to check on the
scullery lads to see how they were coming along
with the scouring of pots and pans, as they were
needed back in the kitchen. On his way through
dimly lit underground corridors, he heard a sound.
Turning down a narrow passageway to investigate,
he happened upon a gentleman, who was overly
involved in sticking his finger down his throat
and retching. The young cook took note that the
man was wearing a livery collar, a designation
that he was in service to the King. Some time
later, he saw the same gentleman. He turned to his
companion, "Who would that gentleman be?"
    "That would be the King's taster. The King
never eats anything before his taster samples it
first. Just in case it's poisoned!"
    "Don't people die right off from poisoning?"
    "No, my friend, there are poisons that may
be administered over time. Death comes slowly!"
    "Why not kill the fellow straight away?"
    "If it's done bit by bit, nobody suspects
foul play!"
    The cook did not tell his friend what he had
seen. Instead, he sent a message to the Queen,
saying he had information. Elizabeth met him
secretly and listened intently. She paid the cook
well for his information. "Keep this to yourself.
I will take the necessary steps." However, the
Queen was thoroughly put out with her estranged
husband. In typical fashion, she did not think the
matter through. She did not tell Edward. She did
have her spies make some dispassionate inquires

concerning the food taster. The investigation turned up that he was an associate of James Tyrell, a Northerner who had supported Henry VI. "Well, if Edward was being poisoned it served him right!" She kept her thoughts entirely to herself.

When the gentle winds of May at last arrived, Edward was too ill to lead a summer campaign against Scotland. By June, Edward was feeling somewhat better, at least well enough to meet with Richard at Fotheringhay. The Duchess of York was glad to have her two sons with her.

Cecily saw Richard and his family, but she seldom went to London. Elizabeth detested the Dowager Duchess. When Cecily greeted Edward in the inner courtyard, she was immediately concerned by Edward's appearance. Edward brushed it off as a bad case of the flue he was unable to shake. The King proceeded with Richard to their mother's private quarters. Edward laid out his strategy. "It is left up to you alone, Richard. I need a victory! The Scots need to be put to rest!"

"What may I count on?"

"I will provide you with surgeons and two thousand men, which I will raise by indenture. They will bring an imposing arsenal from the Tower of London." Edward wiped sweat from his brow, as though it was the middle of summer. "You will have an unexpected ally in the Duke of Albany, James III's brother." Edward smiled in his familiar way. "On the one hand, I am able to sympathize with the Scottish king. On the other, I am not adverse to using his brother's treason to our advantage."

"I will marshal the troops at Alnwick Castle rather than at Sheriff Hutten. This will keep Henry Percy more involved in the campaign."

"How many men in arms do you plan to march north with?"

"Twenty thousand!"

"Your first objective will be the town of Berwick. While Queen Margaret surrendered it to the Scots, there are still many Englishmen behind the city's walls. It may capitulate, providing you with a quick victory. We will borrow Louis XI's innovation. We will set up couriers along the road from the Marches to London. In this way, each man will gallop a short distance and deliver his message to the next courier." Edward smiled. "News of your triumph will arrive speedily to the citizens of London."

"Are there sufficient funds to stock the supply lines?"

"Only if you go in, hit hard and return in haste."

Before leaving Fotheringhay, Edward was feeling significantly better. The Duchess of York wanted Edward to remain under her care for a bit longer. She knew instinctively that something was wrong. Edward refused his mother's offer; he had to return to London.

Richard and Henry Percy amassed their forces, marching without delay to Berwick. Edward was right! Berwick surrendered with the exception of the castle. Richard left Lord Stanley behind to continue the assault on the castle while he pursued the Scottish King.

The Scottish King was not fairing well. His lords, tired of suffering loses for the French King, had revolted. James' favorites were hung from Lauder Bridge; James himself was being held captive at Edinburgh Castle. Richard attempted to invoke the Scottish lords into battle by burning villages, but to no avail.

At the end of July, Richard entered Edinburgh without resistance. The Duke of Albany pleaded with Richard to prevent the English troops from looting the city. Richard commanded sufficient respect! His men obeyed his command, forfeiting their medieval rights as soldiers to benefit from a victory by pillaging the citizenry.

The Scottish lords sent word to Richard that they were submitting and asked for Richard's terms. The most Richard was able to obtain without a military victory and insufficient funding was a Scottish truce. The pledge that Edward's daughter, Cecily, was to marry James III's son was renewed. Richard assessed the situation; the Scots would not accept the Duke of Albany as their king, anymore than the English had been willing to take the Duke of Clarence on as their king. Instead, Richard requested that the Duke of Albany be fully reinstated in exchange for his oath of allegiance to James III.

The Scots had only been brought to heel! Richard marched back to Berwick, the fortressed city on the sea. In a display of military grandeur before the entire host of his company, Richard bestowed honors on Lord Stanley and knighthood on men who had illustriously proven themselves in the campaign. After handing out remunerations, most of the men were sent home.

By the end of August, Richard took Berwick Castle. Richard dispatched the courier who rode hard with the news to the next station south, handed his communication to the second messenger, and so on until word reached London. Gloucester's victory was heralded through the city as if he had taken Paris. Edward was ecstatic! A grateful Parliament granted Richard Carlisle Castle and he was made Warden of the West Marches for life.

The Christmas season of 1482 was a jubilant affair. Richard, Duke of Gloucester, entered London to the cheers of the populace. He received hearty congratulations from the Parliament, lords and commons alike. Edward was well pleased. He saw to it that the holiday celebrations swelled to magnificent proportions. Edward's beautiful daughters showed off the latest fashions; satin gowns encrusted with jewels, wide necklines and large puffy sleeves. Edward was the jovial host, parading his brother so all might see the vanquisher of the Scots. Plays, disguisings, music, dancing and troubadours abounded. Clarions and trumpets announced lords, ladies and foreign dignitaries. Minstrels played throughout the many courses of seemingly unending banquets.

Edward's elation was not to last! Not long after Richard's arrival, disparaging news arrived from across the Channel. Louis XI was pressing through Artois towards Flanders and Calais. Maximllian and Mary had been forced to sign a treaty with the French King. Margaret, their young daughter, was to marry the Dauphin, who had been promised to Princess Elizabeth. Louis stopped paying his yearly stipend of 50,000 gold crowns to Edward. Burgundy's trade was under French control. France had emerged as a great nation!

The indignity of Burgundy's loss did not affect the Duke of Gloucester. Everyone knew that he was one of but a few men who opposed Edward's decision to sign a treaty with Louis XI, rather than engage the French in combat. Edward fell into a deep melancholy. Not even food pleased him!

Richard was worried! He waited to leave London until the end of February, when the King's constitution appeared to improve. After a brief sojourn in York, Richard set out for Middleham.

Edward, just ten-years-old, had been watching for his father from the viewing platform above the Great Hall. He had a delicate frame, like his mother, which was weakened further by the close proximity of bloodlines between his parents. He was prone to catching colds, but his spirit, like his father's, was strong but gentler in nature. The boy's benevolence endeared him most of all to his father. When the distinctive white boar banner came into view, Edward hurried down the spiral staircase to grab a warmer coat before descending the outer staircase from the great keep and into the inner courtyard. Soldiers acknowledged him as he ran under the gatehouse and over the drawbridge. Above him, guards on the battlements were preparing for Richard's arrival. When Edward reached the small tower, the guardsmen greeted him. "You'll be warmer if you go back to the gatehouse to wait for your father."

"You'll have a better view as well!"

Edward headed back amidst a flurry of activity. He climbed the stairs to the captain's quarters. The Captain was a broad-shouldered man with raven black hair and beard, who had fought side by side with Richard at Tewkesbury. "Sit down young Earl, right here by the fire and warm yourself. We'll let you know when your father crosses the drawbridge.

Edward smiled gratefully. "Thank you for your hospitality, and you don't have to call me Earl."

The Captain laughed! The young Earl of Salisbury rubbed his small hands together to warm them. "Captain, do you think my father will be staying at Middleham long?"

"We'll soon find out. If it was up to your father, he'd be here with you more often than not."

It wasn't long before Richard was in the inner courtyard. Edward had left the gatehouse and stood waiting for him impatiently. Richard smiled widely, dismounted and caught his son up in his arms. Richard kissed his son then looked upon him with tender eyes. "I have missed you!"

"Father, will you be staying?"

"Without question!" Richard had plenty to do in the North! Enough to keep him busy for the remainder of his days!

Anne ran out nervously looking for her son. "It's cold! Both of you come inside!"

168

Death of the King

Shortly after Easter, the forty-year-old Edward collapsed during a fishing trip. Within a few days, it looked as if he was recovering, but then became weaker with each successive day. On April 8th, as if a cloud had been lifted from his mind, he lucidly assessed the situation he was leaving behind. He called for Hastings, his stepsons, the Queen's brothers, but not the Queen! Though he was weak, he sought to appeal to the generosity of their spirit asking them to put their pettiness aside. An aid propped up his pillow. "I am dying! I am speaking to you as a friend and an Englishman, not as your king. I implore you with all the strength I am able to rally, heed my words. Unless you love one another, England will be destroyed in civil war. All that you hold true and precious will be lost."

Lachrymose, the men were faced with the immediacy of Edward's demise. Sobbing, Hastings and Dorset embraced, promising to love one another. Despondently, the others followed suit. While his body was weakening, Edward's mind was becoming clearer. He thought to himself. "I have been asleep! Negligent in my duties! Not one man present is capable of keeping the realm intact!" When his friends had left, he asked his aid to summon the five executors of his will. "Queen Elizabeth is to be dropped; Lord Stanley added!"

The following day, Edward's secretary transcribed Edward's last words while his executors bore witness. "My debts are all to be paid. Any rectifications made!" Edward paused to catch his breath. "Allocate a generous portion of my goods to the poor." Edward, sweating profusely, considered naming his brother the heir to the throne, but his pride stepped in the way.

Richard could be counted upon to do the impossible. After himself, Richard was the foremost general in the realm. "Richard, Duke of Gloucester, is named sole Protector of Edward, Prince of Wales and the realm." No one present was particularly surprised!

After his will was signed and sealed, Edward sent them away and called for the priests, who were waiting immediately outside the chamber door with scented oils, holy water, the Eucharist and a clean, white cloth. Edward made his last confession, turning his thoughts and heart to God. His major organs were shutting down. At first he was attentive to the odd, almost numbing sensations. Then he slowly lost awareness of his body. He was slipping into unconsciousness much as if he was going to sleep, but this time it was different. His life surprisingly flashed before him in an instant. How quickly it had all gone!

With his last breath, Edward's soul left through the top of his head. At first, he was not aware that he was dead. His form was like his physical body, only healthier, fit and more vibrant with color. Amazed, Edward spoke to the priests, "I am all right!"

The priests failed to acknowledge him and were completely unaware of his presence. Edward took notice of what was totally occupying their attention. The priests were washing and anointing the physical form he had just left. He noticed that standing nearby were two figures, familiar but out of the ordinary at the same time. At first he was startled, then relieved. Beyond the priests stood his father and Edmund. "Brother, we have come to show you the way."

Edward felt joy and love that he had not known for a long time. He asked, "Where are we going?"

Edmund spoke, "We are going to walk this land with you so that you might be fully aware of the conditions that you helped to create."

The Duke and Edmund securely held Edward's hands as they slipped through Westminster Palace and through time. Edward watched a younger version of himself, intoxicated with wine with a young maiden on his arm. The Duke spoke, "What occupies the Queen's attention?"

Edward had never considered the question before. They found the Queen scantly dressed in her chambers. One of her ladies was just finishing her hair. Elizabeth dismissed her! Shortly afterwards, a tall, strapping, light-haired gentleman was escorted into the apartments by one of the Queen's sisters. The Duke spoke, "Meet the father of the Prince of Wales!"

Edward was surprised! "Is this young Richard's father as well?"

"No, my brother!"

The Duke interjected, "Remember the measles you had as a young man?" Edward nodded. "That illness left you incapable of fathering children of your own. Did you not wonder why, with all of your many affairs, that you fathered no bastard children?"

"Brother, what you call angels attempted to impress upon you, to name our brother, Richard, heir to the throne."

"Why did they not pound it into my head?"

"It is not the way of God or Holy Spirit. Free choice is always yours!"

"Richard is to be King?" queried Edward. His vantage point from the Otherside of the Veil had changed his perspective of the physical world.

"It is difficult to make changes in the physical world from this dimension. Nonetheless, we will visit Stillington. Hopefully, you will be able to impress upon the Bishop to break his oath to you so that Richard hears the truth."

They found Bishop Stillington uneasy. Word of Edward's critical illness had been brought to his attention. Would God forgive him if he broke his oath to King Edward? Would God forgive him if he didn't? Edward was surprised that they were able to hear Stillington's thoughts.

"It is complicated! Be it said that in the world you have just left, the mind, body and emotions are separate. In this world of spirit they are not! Because you are in this world, the laws of this world prevail."

Edward moved close to the Bishop, who felt a chill on his shoulders. Stillington shuddered slightly. Edmund laughed, "Really get his attention! Walk through him!"

Bishop Stillington's entire body went cold as Edward passed from front to back. Edward directed his thoughts to the side of the Bishops head, about three inches above his right ear. Edward poured out his heart. "I free you from your oath. Go to Richard! Tell him the truth! Richard is rightfully the next in line to the crown."

Stillington became more solicitous. The Duke patted Edward on the back, "Well done!"

"How's that?"

Edmund found military vocabulary the best way to explain matters to Edward. "Are you able to feel how Stillington's presence goes beyond his physical form?"

"I can see it!"

"This quality is something like a battleground, where when one element from either side is altered, it changes the field as well as the outcome. Because you have gotten through to Stillington, there is a pathway of energy that was not there before. Events are already cascading around the new pattern."

The trio visited Richard, who was mindlessly checking his saddle leathers. The Duke spoke, "It is upon Richard's shoulders to complete the work that I promised and you began."

Edward spoke. "With my blessings, the realm is bequeathed to you."

Disturbed, Richard had a feeling that something had happened to Edward. Uneasiness consumed him! He dismissed it! It was illogical; Edward had the resilient constitution of a bear!

After briefly visiting several others, they returned to Edward's deathbed. Edward's father nodded to a large vortex of swirling white lights within which were large, beautiful beings. The old Duke and Edmund still had Edward firmly by the hands. They were not about ready to let go.

The old Duke spoke, "Your work is complete."

Edmund nodded towards the Light, "Think of it as one of the magnificent paved roads the Romans left behind. The journey will take, what will seem to you, three days."

"What is our objective?"

"You are still the general!" Edmund laughed! "Our first destination will be to a place of healing and incomparable wonder. Sweet meadows, rolling hills, lush forests, fresh, clean waterfalls and lakes."

Edward looked back one last time. The priests were yet busy with his body. They had removed his clothes. A white cloth covered his remains from the waist to the knees. Edward took notice of what looked like a black, murky puddle on the floor. "What is that?"

The old Duke shuddered, "That, my son, is a mantle wrought by naïve but, nonetheless, rancorous minds. You wore it in life and only recently, relinquished it from your person. It is being left behind!"

They stepped into the current of light. Edward was surprised to find that it had more than palpability; it had presence. Miraculously, he was enveloped by wondrous love and joy, the likes of which he never felt even in the most exuberant moments of his impassioned life. They moved through a white tunnel flanked by angels. Edward became progressively more cognizant of his greater

173

self. The old Duke looked to Edward as he transformed slowly into a younger version of himself. "Edward, it will be your choice, but you will be asked to return to help your brothers."

"As you have helped me?"

"Not exactly!"

Bells tolled out the news of the King's death. Rumors spread that Edward had been poisoned. The Queen clandestinely called her kin to her. The solemn pact the Woodvilles had made at Edward's deathbed was cast asunder. Commons, nobles and gentry grieved. The old adage that had proved so true during the minority reign of Henry VI, "Woe to the land whose ruler is a child." Was often whispered.

It wasn't until the middle of April that a courier dispatched by Lord Hastings arrived at Middleham with the disparaging news. Richard read the laconic letter with disbelief. "Edward IV, your brother, is dead. He left everything under your protection. Secure Prince Edward and get you to London!"

His first reaction was anger at his brother for dying too soon, leaving him with an unfeasible task. Richard, Edward IV's Lieutenant of the North, had reigned as king of the North without the title of monarch. But now, his retreat and life as he had enjoyed it had ended forever. His world was in upheaval and so he guessed correctly, was the state. Guilty at the rage he felt, Richard dealt with his fury in the only way he knew - he stuffed it! He was almost gratified when his resentment was replaced by remorse. This satisfaction bothered him as well. Middleham's entire household changed into black garments!

Richard dispatched a letter of inquiry to Anthony Woodville, Earl River, at Ludlow. "As Protector and uncle of Edward V, I wish to honor his sovereign by entering the capitol with him. When and by what route will you be traveling with the young King?"

Several days later, a courier arrived at Middleham, not from Earl River, but from Lord Hastings. "The Queen and her family are planning on taking control of Prince Edward by having him crowned immediately. When that occurs, your position, as Protector will cease. I have managed through fierce negotiations to limit the Prince's escort to two thousand men. Secure the King!"

Richard called John Kendall. He dictated a bold message to the members who had formed Edward's council. "I served Edward IV with the utmost loyalty and intend to do the same for Edward V. The new government by precedent will be established justly and under the law. According to that law, the dead King's last will and testament must be upheld. Anything contrary to Edward IV's last wishes must and will be judged criminal."

As Richard's messenger clattered across the drawbridge towards London, a courier arrived from Wales with a letter from Henry Stafford, Duke of Buckingham. "I put myself and my army at your service. What would you have me do?"

Next to Richard, Buckingham was the noblest lord in the land. Though disgruntled with the Queen, he had neither entered the political arena, nor succumbed to the social squabbling and squandering of Edward's court. Richard dictated a letter to Buckingham. "I am leaving shortly with a small company of friends and retainers. It would please me to have you join our company, but bring only three hundred men at the most." Before departing, Richard administered the oath of fealty to King Edward V to those accompanying him and the officers of the city of York.

On the road to Nottingham a courier from Earl Rivers delivered a message to Richard. "The King and I will be leaving Ludlow Castle on April 24th. We should arrive in Northampton on the 29th. It would please us to have the Duke of Gloucester join us."

Richard sent word back that he was in accord. Simultaneously, a second message from Buckingham arrived stating that he was on the way. A third message arrived from Lord Hastings. "The Queen, and her brothers, Sir Edward and Lionel, Bishop of Salisbury, along with the Queen's eldest son, the Marques of Dorset, have captured the council. They are ignoring your Protectorship! They plan to crown Edward immediately to keep power in their hands. My life is in danger as I have championed your cause."

Feeling in control, the Queen sent word to her brother, Earl Rivers. "I am in charge of the realm. Make haste to London with Prince Edward so that he might be crowned straight away and the Protectorship ended."

Though the council they had assembled was illegal, it was under their control! Dorset proceeded to appoint his uncle, Sir Edward Woodville, Commander of the fleet. In addition, he gave Sir Edward a portion of the treasury. The remainder he divided between his mother and himself.

Hastings responded by having Richard's declaration to the dead King's Council distributed throughout Britain and the Continent. The letter both calmed the worries of the citizens and inspired trust in Edward's brother. Support for the Protector was growing. It was commonly heard, "The Duke of Gloucester deserves the government!"

Dorest's arrogance was all that reigned supreme, "We are so important that even without the King's uncle we can make and enforce our decisions." He sent a dispatch to Earl Rivers that Price Edward must be in London by May 1st.

Richard and his party rode into Northampton on April 29th to learn that Edward V's party had not waited for him, but had gone ahead to Stony Stratford. As he was making preparations for his men, Earl Rivers arrived in Northampton accompanied by a few men. Seeking out Richard, he bowed, explaining, "Northampton is too small to accommodate both of our parties. I settled Prince Edward and my men at Stony Stratford. In this way, we might all spend a pleasant and comfortable evening."

"It is thoughtful of you! Buckingham will be arriving shortly. You will join us for dinner!"

As Buckingham approached Northampton, he thought and rethought his position. He hated the Woodvilles and his wife, whom he considered far beneath his station! However, he and his family had cause against the Yorks. His paternal grandfather had been killed on the outskirts of Northampton fighting for Henry VI over twenty years ago. His father and maternal grandfather, the Duke of Somerset, died at St. Albans in 1455. What he knew for certain was that he could not take on both the Woodvilles and the house of York. For the moment, he chose the lesser of his two personal demons. Buckingham cast his lot with Richard, gambling that the majority of the lords and commons would prefer Richard to the Woodvilles. He, however, would do what he could to keep his options open.

Everyone knew that a transition from a king to a minority rule was tricky. The current overt restlessness throughout the realm was testimony to that fact. Lords and gentry surrounded themselves with trusted men at arms. Well so! History had proven that boy kings brought out the worst in those who lusted after power. The minority reigns of Richard II and Henry VI had wrought turmoil across the land. Edward IV had failed to keep the Woodvilles in check, or tabs on the Prince of Wales. Only by the last minute change in his will naming Richard as Protector, had the King averted outright civil war. Whatever a man might say for certain was that anything might happen!

Buckingham arrived in the middle of dinner. Jovial, he kept the conversation light. Only after Earl Rivers retired, did he speak with Richard sympathetically, but in earnest. Before retiring, John Kendall had transcribed written orders for Richard and Buckingham's captains.

Early in the morning, Richard and Buckingham, along with their men, set out for Stony Stratford. They left guards behind to detain Earl Rivers and his escort. Outriders were sent ahead to barricade the roads going out of Stony Stratford. When Richard arrived, Edward V's party was packed, mounted and ready to depart. Richard and Buckingham dismounted and paid their respects to the young King, who was flanked by Sir Thomas Vaughan and Lord Richard Grey. Richard's presence held sway. "Edward, as your Protector I wish to speak with you of urgent news."

Grey and Vaughn followed the young King. When they entered the inn, Edward V's advisors were arrested and taken to Yorkshire where they were detained. After reassuring Edward, Richard walked back out into the city's streets. He addressed the two thousand men accompanying Edward. "The King has been delivered safely into the Protector's watch. You are all dismissed! Return to your homes!" Without a leader and unwilling to engage the Duke of Gloucester in combat, they took leave of Stony Stratford.

Richard, Buckingham and Edward V returned to Northampton. Upon his arrival, Richard dictated a letter explaining his actions. It was sent off to London to be posted by Lord Hastings.

James Tyrell's man reached the capitol first. The Queen was awakened in the middle of the night! Hysterical, she sent for Dorset. Frantically, they called the lords to array armies so that together for the purpose of besieging and compelling the hostile Duke of Gloucester into relinquishing King Edward V. No one answered the call! No one was interested in helping the Queen!

Elizabeth, her brother, Lionel, Bishop of Salisbury, along with the five royal princesses and the Duke of York sought sanctuary in Westminster Abbey. They took whatever Sir Edward Woodville had not plundered from the royal treasury, along with Edward's personal wealth and goods. Thomas Rotherham, Archbishop of York, seized the Great Seal of England. When he brought it to the Queen, he found a gigantic, gapping hole in the wall of the Abbey, through which cartloads of booty were being delivered to the Queen.

Hastings sent word to Richard. "It is safe for you to enter London. All cheerfully anticipate your arrival. Alas, Rotherham has taken the Great Seal to Edward's widow."

Richard sent a message to the Archbishop of Canterbury. "I request you heartily to make safe the Great Seal. Provide for the security of the Tower of London and safeguard the treasury. We plan to arrive in London on Sunday, May 4th."

Richard turned his attention to Edward V. "Word has come that your mother and her kin have been unable to raise men to march against me. I am not saying this to frighten you. Rather, it clearly demonstrates the Woodville's unpopularity. You are to be king of all England. Dispensing justice with a fair hand, without favoritism, creates good government. If your bias is for one court faction or another, civil war is likely to break out. Your father foresaw this. That is why he made me Protector for your sake, as well as the welfare of the entire realm. Do you understand?"

Tears welled up in Edward's eyes. Richard softened. "Is there something you wish taken care of, as your first act as sovereign?"

Edward was put at ease. "Yes, I would like to reward my chaplain, John Geffrey."

Richard smiled, "First of all, we have to summon John Kendall so that he might transcribe your royal command." Edward smiled! Richard's secretary was sent for. "Now, you must decide on how to honor your chaplain."

"He has told me that he would like to be appointed rector of a parish church."

"We will compose a letter to the custodian of the seal of the earldom of March, asking that he write to the Bishop of Hereford on behalf of your request." Edward sighed.

The new King's party entered London, escorted only by a few hundred men. Richard and Buckingham were attired in black. They flanked Edward V, who wore blue velvet. Crowds cheered their new sovereign, but were more gratified to note that the Duke of Gloucester was clearly in charge. After escorting Edward V to the palace of the Bishop of London, Richard retired to Crosby's Place, his townhouse in Bishopsgate Street. The coronation was delayed! How he was going to extend the Protectorship was another matter? For the sake of the entire realm, Edward V's crowning must be delayed until he is of age? Lords were already lining up to honor Edward V, making their bid for preference, position and power!

Richard administered, to the lords and London's city officials, a solemn oath of fealty to Edward V. It was the first step in establishing the new government. Afterwards, he summoned his first Council, magnanimously including those who had supported the Woodvilles. Lord Hastings, who had enjoyed a wide sphere of power and popularity because of his camaraderie with Edward IV, found his position slipping to the Duke of Buckingham, and John Howard. Unlike Hastings neither men had participated in Edward IV's debauchedness. Buckingham had the Protector's ear. Howard was much like Richard — a skillful general, charitable, concerned with the wellbeing of his tenants, he loved music and was well read. Howard moved easily into the intimate, confidential circle that met often with the Protector at Crosby's Place. Lords and loyalties reshuffled! Lord Hastings found himself in an uneasy alignment with Morton, Bishop of Ely, and Rotherham, Archbishop of York, as well as Lord Stanley.

In compliance with Edward IV's will, the Council invested Richard with the power of Protector. The mandate created Richard as a temporary monarch without the title of king. Though the Protector and Council organized the government with modest changes, the base of power was ultimately reordered! The Great Seal was bestowed on John Russell, Bishop of Lincoln. Richard's friend, John Wode, who had been Speaker of the Commons, was made Treasurer. James Tyrell, along with Richard Ratcliffe and Robert Brackenbury, were added to Richard's personal household. William Catesby switched his loyalties from Hastings to the Protector. Hastings watched his power slipping!

At the first Council meeting, the amiable Duke of Buckingham stepped forward to suggest that Edward V be moved to the royal apartments in the Tower of London. It was decided that Rivers, Vaughan and Grey remain in prison. The question of how to coax the Queen out of Westminster Abbey remained unresolved. Sir Edward Woodville was declared a traitor. However, a full pardon would be granted to any sailor who deserted him.

Lord Howard, an accomplished diplomat and captain, was appointed the task of attaining Edward IV's fleet from Sir Edward Woodville. Initially, Howard and his captains circulated the Protector's proclamation amongst the captains and sailors. Sir Edward's Italian commanders, not wishing to cause offense to England's new government, rationed out the entire stock of wine and beer to the sailors. After the men passed out or were sufficiently drunk, the Genoese captains declared for the Protector. Sir Edward escaped to Brittany with two vessels, as well as a good portion of the royal treasure. Henry Tudor was elated!

The estate holdings of Buckingham were in the politically troubled Wales and Welsh Marches. In mid May, Richard invested Buckingham with offices, which in effect, made him viceroy of Wales. Earl Rivers' office of Chief Butler of England was bestowed upon Francis Lovell, whom Edward IV had made a viscount.

While Richard was doing his best to be evenhanded, lords and factions were daily paying court to Edward V at the Tower of London. It wasn't difficult to foresee the enormous problems that would be created if Edward V were crowned before coming of age. Feeling that he had the majority of public support behind him, Richard offered the suggestion that the Protectorship be continued.

Anne, Duchess of Gloucester, arrived at Crosby's Palace on June 5th. Robert Stillington, the Bishop of Bath and Wells, arrived shortly afterwards, seeking a private audience with Richard. Richard had listened to many men in a month's time; he was open to hearing the Bishop's input. Stillington began quietly, but with sincerity. "I married your brother, Edward."

Richard looked up a bit surprised. "To Elizabeth Woodville?"

"No, to Lady Eleanor Butler!"

Uncharacteristically, Richard sputtered out, "When?"

"Before he married Elizabeth!"

Richard was stunned. "The Pope gave him permission to divorce Lady Eleanor?"

"No! Edward never got divorced! Edward's children are illegitimate! It is my duty to come forth and speak the truth so that England's rightful king will ascend to the throne."

"What proof have you?"

"This marriage document!"

Richard looked at the document. "You are the one who signed it! What other evidence is there?"

The Bishop handed Richard several letters. "I had told your brother, George. George took the matter up with Edward when he was arrested. This, I know to be true, because Edward questioned me after George's death. Edward knew I was the only one who could have informed George. I was immediately fined and then confined in the White Tower for several months." The Bishop hesitated. "Your brother, Edward, made me declare a solemn oath never to tell anyone else. However, he is dead and the true king must take the throne. May God forgive my soul!" Richard called in John Kendall and members of his staff, asking them to check out the Bishop's story.

At Edward IV's death, Jane Shore relented; she became the mistress of the Marques of Dorset. Commiserating the loss of their sphere of influence with Edward's death, it was Jane, who came up with an idea. "The Woodvilles are unable to overthrow Richard alone. Why not patch your relations with Hastings? If you manage this, Morton, Rotherham and Stanley will follow!"

Dorset agreed! Jane found her way to the bed of Lord Hastings. Hastings, mesmerized by love, agreed in the heat of passion that he would be a better Protector than Richard. Afterwards, he conspired with Morton, Rotherham and Stanley. It was determined that Jane was to take word of their plot to Queen Elizabeth.

The plot was discovered by a man in the service of Buckingham, who readily brought word of the insurrection to Richard. Richard felt the sorrow of betrayal of Hastings. As for Stanley, Richard was appalled at the man's penchant for treachery. Buckingham waited for an opening and spoke. "You will have to make an example if the Protectorship is to continue."

"Stanley and Dorset will be tried for treason and sent to the headsman."

Buckingham managed to keep his personal options open by talking Richard into sacrificing Hastings and Rivers. Buckingham was close in age to Richard. However, he had spent more time at court; thus, he understood all of the king's men well, too well. Hastings and Rivers would never support his efforts to become king. More likely, they could be persuaded to join Richard.

Richard sent for John Kendall. He dictated letters appealing to the loyalty of his friends in the North to send troops. He entrusted the messages to Richard Radcliffe, who rode out from London on June 10th.

On the morning of June 13th, Richard called two meetings. Chancellor Russell met with members of the Council at Westminster to plan the coronation. Hastings, Morton, Rotherham and Stanley, as well as other advisors, met in the Tower of London. Those in attendance noticed that there were more Yeomen about than usual. Richard was already seated, facing the door as the men approached the table. The usher shut the door, giving a nod to the Protector. When everyone was seated Richard opened the meeting. "A plot against the government has been uncovered. The Queen, Shore's wife and others are involved." The room turned ice cold. Richard looked directly at the conspirators. "Hastings, Morton, Rotherham and Stanley! The four of you are charged with treason."

When the usher heard the word 'treason' he opened the door and a company of Yeomen quickly filled the chamber. "Men, arrest Morton and Rotherham! Escort them to prison cells. Take Stanley to his own quarters! Keep a guard on him! Bring a priest for Lord Hastings that he might prepare his soul before being executed."

'Treason' reverberated through the Tower complex. Rumors ran rampant in the streets of London. Commerce, work, and for that matter, all activities came rapidly to a halt! Shortly, a royal herald and trumpeter were dispatched into the city. "The government is secure. By the authority of the Royal Council, Lord Hastings, the leader of the conspiracy, has been executed."

Calm settled over the city. Whispers circulated that the Protector would assume the crown. Jane Shore was obliged to do public penance. Hasting's body was taken to the Chapel of St. George in Windsor Castle, where in accord with Edward IV's will, Hastings was buried near him. Richard took Katherine Woodville, Hasting's widow, under his protection and granted her Hasting's estates.

Buckingham counseled Richard to have Rivers, Vaughan and Grey executed on charges of treason. "Four heads are a small price to pay for a peaceful transition in government." He also asked Richard for the custody of Bishop Ely.

As the Queen was a conspirator, the Archbishop of Canterbury was sent to fetch Prince Richard. He found the Queen fitful, almost to the point of panic. "What will Richard have of me?"

"I am to secure the young Prince Richard."

Elizabeth Woodville started. "What will he do with my young son?"

"Your son will be safe!"

"Trust Richard? He will seek revenge against me through my sons."

"Madam, you do not have a choice. By your implication in treason, you have put your kin and advisors at risk. Hastings has already met his Maker! To keep the headcount at a minimal, I would boldly suggest that you place your youngest son in the care of the Protector."

Left with little choice, the Queen consented. Nine-year-old Prince Richard left the Abbey, holding onto the much larger hand of the Archbishop. His heart beat so loudly in his chest that he thought surely everyone could hear. After meeting briefly with his uncle, the boy's mind was somewhat put to rest. Afterwards, he was taken to his brother, Edward V. To his immense relief, Prince Richard found Edward studying Latin with his tutor in the royal apartments.

Edward, Earl of Warwick, the Duke of Clarence's ten-year-old, mentally retarded son, had been placed in the care of Anne, Duchess of Gloucester. She had left both her son and her ward in Middleham. Like Richard, she missed her son dearly, but he was not yet strong enough to travel the long journey to the capitol. London kept Anne's mind occupied. Many were already paying her court. For the second time in her life, the prospect of becoming queen loomed in her future. She was reminded of her first husband. Richard was by far preferable of the two, but Richard was also partially responsible for her father's death.

The rebellion was stopped early, but many felt threatened by a re-visitation of a turbulent minority rule. Others wanted Edward V crowned. Rumors persisted that Richard would be declared king. Anne and England were both torn!

Richard III

We never know how high we are,
'Til we are called to rise.
And then if we are true to plan,
Our statures touch the skies.
The heroism we recite,
Would be a daily thing.
Did not ourselves the cupid's warp
For fear to be a king.

Emily Dickinson

London was abuzz with information, rumor, speculation, doubt and fear. The difficulty lay in determining what was what! Hastings men had entered the service of the Duke of Buckingham. It was rumored that a massive army was marching towards London from the North. Though Edward V and Prince Richard were observed daily playing on the Tower Green, many doubted that the boy would be crowned King. The street talk, however, inspired neither riots nor protests. Rather, King Edward IV's brother's reputation offered comfort to most; fear to some. Order was instilled with little effort. Confidence prevailed that the safety of the realm was in capable hands!

In France the wily Louis XI was doing his best to defer death with the purchase of indulgences, gifting alms to the poor, and by numerous petitions to a variety of saints. It was to no avail; he was dying. Edward IV's death brought him no pleasure. It was only a reminder that all men meet their Creator without formality of title, estate or wealth. Louis was terrified!

In England Richard had received confirmation from trusted advisors that the documents and letters provided by the Bishop of Bath and Wells were legitimate. The Tower records showed that for several months, the Bishop had been in residence in a cell after George's execution. Richard laid this evidence and his claim to the throne before the Council for their opinion. Howard and Buckingham were the first to stand up, expressing approval. Many were relieved for a way out of the minority rule.

Richard sent word to York to delay the march into London. Rather than a show of force, he was determined to rule by consent. To prepare people for the change, Richard wore royal purple when he rode through the city that day. Members of the Council spread the word through their particular circles of influence of Edward's precontract. Soon word was out on the street.

The following day, Sunday, June 22, 1483, Richard, accompanied by an array of lords, rode to Paul's Cross, a spot where public information was disseminated. That day, many gathered to hear the fluent Friar Ralph Shaa speak. He began with a quote from the Old Testament, "Bastard slips shall not take root." Pausing, he allowed his words to take full effect. "There is sufficient evidence to prove that our beloved Edward IV had already entered into a precontract of marriage at the time he married Elizabeth Woodville."

Many in the crowd had already heard the rumor. In spite of efforts to keep it hushed, gossip had persisted for years that Edward IV was the son of Edward Blayborgue. It was just surprising to hear the accusation spoken publicly from the mayor's brother, a man revered for honesty, as well as humility. The Friar reminded the crowd of the Duke of Gloucester's character, bravery and accomplishments. "As the Duke of Clarence had been convicted of treason, his son is not eligible to inherit the crown. Richard is rightfully the next in line to the throne!"

Loquaciously but elegantly, on Monday, Lord Buckingham stood before the House of Lords touting Richard's aptitudes. On Wednesday, a joint session of the Lords and Commons unanimously approved the ascension of Richard III to the throne of England. On Thursday, June 26th, a great crowd of nobility and commoners gathered up and down the streets around Baynard's Castle. Buckingham loudly read the petition that had been drawn up by Parliament the day before, requesting Richard to assume the scepter. When Buckingham was finished, he looked up and smiled charmingly at Richard.

Richard humbly accepted, mounted his horse and rode to Westminster Hall followed by all of London. After sitting in the marble chair of the King's Bench, he took the royal oath. Afterwards, he spoke to the justices while throngs of people listened. "I charge you to dispense justice without fear or favor. All men, regardless of station, must stand equal before the law." Then he summoned Sir John Fogge, a sworn enemy of the Yorks, to appear before him. Taking Fogge's hand and holding it high for all to see, Richard spoke, "I swear to be your friend." Fogge was appointed Kent's Justice of the Peace.

The coronation was set for July 6th; there was much to do. John Russell was appointed Chancellor and keeper of the Great Seal. Catesby was named Chancellor of the Exchequer. John Howard was elevated to Duke of Norfolk. Thomas, son of Lord Howard, was made Earl of Surrey. Berkeley was made Earl of Nottingham. Knighthood was bestowed on seventeen gentlemen. At Buckingham's insistence, Lord Stanley was released and returned to his place in the Council.

At the King's request, the Earl of Northumberland arrived on the outskirts of London with only several thousand men. Richard walked without cap of estate or crown through their midst, thanking them for their loyalty and service. Afterwards, they followed Richard into London. They were given the task of serving as military police during the ceremonies. Hoping to avoid any retribution against the Woodvilles, a royal order was sent out charging everyone to put aside old quarrels.

On July 5th, the King and Queen rode in royal procession to the royal apartments at the Tower of London, where they spent the night. In general, people had stopped coming to the Tower to pay Edward homage. Only James Tyrell visited the Princes now and again.

Buckingham had talked Richard into allowing him to be first officer of the coronation, ahead of Norfolk. On July 6th, the King's procession walked the long, red cloth that led up to Westminster Abbey. Heralds and trumpeters walked ahead of a large, tall, elaborate cross. Cardinal Bourchier, followed, flanked by two bishops. Northumberland followed Bourchier, carrying the Sword of Mercy. Behind him walked Lord Stanley with the Constable's mace. Next in the procession was Richard's brother-in-law, John de la Pole, Duke of Suffolk, holding the scepter. Suffolk's eldest son, John Earl of Lincoln, carried the orb. The Duke of Norfolk carried the jeweled crown. Thomas Howard, Earl of Surrey, bore the Sword of State. To Richard's right and left walked Viscount Lovell and the Earl of Kent, who each bore Swords of Justice. Buckingham held Richard's train. Following Buckingham were earls and barons of the realm. Knights and gentry followed the lords.

In the Queen's procession, Stanley's wife, the Countess of Richmond and mother of Henry Tudor, held Anne's train. Every lord and lady in the kingdom was in attendance. The only exceptions were those few who were too young, several who were too bitter, and Lord Buckingham's wife. Everyone dressed in gorgeous attire for the affair!

The royal couple walked to seats of estate in St. Edward's shrine, next to the high altar where they listened to the choir. Afterwards, Richard and Anne walked to the altar. Their robes were taken from them, leaving them standing naked to the waist. After being anointed with the sacred chrism, they were dressed in cloth of gold. Cardinal Bourchier crowned the King and Queen. The mantel Edward IV had worn was secured around Richard's shoulders. Richard and Anne returned to their seats to hear the high mass chanted in Latin verse.

When the ceremonies were completed, the royal couple retired for several hours while the hall was prepared for a sumptuous banquet. Under Buckingham's supervision, everything was perfect. He grinned like a cat holding its prey! His self-importance was ballooning. Like Warwick, what his ego would not allow him to see was that he was like a moon, iridescent in the radiant light of the York sun.

During the meal, Sir Robert Dynmock, the King's Champion, rode into the hall. He was splendidly arraigned in white armor. His horse was attired in white and red silks. "Anyone wishing to challenge King Richard's right to the throne of England speak up now and fight me!"

There were no takers! A cry rose up, "King Richard! Long live King Richard!"

Richard increased the power and duties of his three loyal lords. It was they who propped his throne, just as he had been Edward's prop. Buckingham was made Great Chamberlain of England. Norfolk was appointed Admiral. The wardenship of the Scottish Marches was delegated to Northumberland. Before leaving for progress with his Queen, he entrusted the government to John Russell, Bishop of Lincoln. Richard decided to take Stanley with him so that he could keep an eye on him, in much the same manner that Edward IV had brought the Duke of Clarence with him. A guard was stationed outside of Westminster Abbey to keep an eye on the Queen and princesses.

The *Croyland Chronicle* reported, "The noble Church of the monks at Westminster, and all the neighboring parts, assumed the character of a castle fortress, while men of the greatest austerity were appointed to act as keepers."

Richard dispatched a letter to Francis, Duke of Brittany. The courier Richard sent was advised to address grievances and re-establish trade agreements. He was also to determine Edward Woodville's position. Absolutely no mention was made of Henry Tudor.

Towards the end of July, King Richard and an entourage of secular lords, spiritual advisors, justices, aids and advisors left on progress. Archers and militia were not included. Richard III was determined to rule by approval and blessings from all his subjects.

From Brittany Henry Tudor had let it be known to his supporters that if Edward IV's sons were out of the way, his ascension to throne would be made that much easier. James Tyrell dared not put his plans to paper. Instead, he simply sent back a verbal message. "Tell the Earl of Richmond that I am working on it."

John Morton, Bishop of Ely, was convinced that the Duke of Buckingham would join in an armed revolt against Richard. Tyrell considered the possibility that if Buckingham would so easily change coats, he might be enticed to make the battle go easier. He sought out the Duke.

Buckingham remained in London after Richard's departure, to discover the latest news from Brittany. Tyrell was all too willing to oblige, "The Earl of Richmond would like to strike soon. He will attack from the south with a fleet supplied to him by the Duke of Brittany. A few of my men are going to take care of the princes in the Tower. It is up to you to raise an army in Wales to confront Richard. He is traveling sparsely. If you move quietly and quickly, he will not have time to gather his supporters. The Woodvilles' army from Kent and Surry will take London."

"How are you planning on getting into the royal apartments at the Tower?"

"With your help!"

"I would suggest that you go before dawn when the Tower staff is busy rising and setting about their tasks. The day before, I will entrust you with the key." Keys to the Tower hung on Buckingham's person. He instinctively patted the keys! "I will see to the guards. Before the day is out, you must give the keys to my servant so that they are returned to me."

This was more than Tyrell had hoped for. "I swear!"

"Another thing! Do no harm to the boys while they are in the Tower! It is too risky!"

Before dawn on an already warm August morning, four of Tyrell's men rowed a boat down the Thames to the Tower. Three men disembarked by the bridge. One carried a satchel. The fourth man watched the boat as the other three made their way to the royal apartments. Buckingham had done his job well; no one was around to stop them. Once in the bedchamber, they found the Princes sleeping. How easy it would be to simply smoother them, but their orders had been precise. Two of the men approached each of the sleeping boys. Nodding to one another, they each put one hand over one of the boy's mouths and the other they held up to their lips in a gesture to remain quiet. One of the men whispered, "We are friends of your departed father, the good King Edward IV. We are here to help you escape. Your uncle wishes you harm."

193

"An army is being raised on your behalf, Your Majesty."

The third man reached into his bundle. "Here put on the clothes of a commoner so that no one takes notice of you."

The boys were escorted unrecognized to the river. Quickly, they entered the boat! Hastily, they departed! Quietly, the men rowed down the Thames! When they moored the boat in the middle of nowhere, Edward became suspicious. The landing site was a curious choice as there was no one to greet them. Two of the men each took the hand of one of the princes, and the third man followed. The fourth stayed behind to watch the boat.

So that he would not have to look in the boy's eyes, the third man came up behind Edward, stabbing him in the back, piercing his heart. Richard's abductor held his hand tightly over the 10-year old Prince's mouth. The third man used the same knife to slit Richard's throat.

The bodies were then taken to the abode of a singularly unusual woman who, as rumor had it, performed black magic. To throw guilt upon Richard III without drawing suspicion to the perpetrators, the bodies were brought back to the Tower in a wooden chest in the dead of night. Buckingham had made arrangements for renovations to begin on the staircase outside the White Tower. The men placed the box in the hole, then covered it up. Buckingham took care of the rest in the morning.

When told about the black magic, Henry Tudor was furious! Plans to expose the bodies and implicate Richard III were scrapped. Henry wanted nothing to do with conjured corpses.

The rebellion itself was made up of strange and strained relationships. There were those in the south and west, who loved Edward IV. They wanted to see Edward's own blood on the throne, as did the Woodvilles. Some men were out of a job with the reorganization of government. Lancastrians wanted to place Henry Tudor on the throne. Henry, Duke of Buckingham, had his own furtive ambition to be king. Every faction knew of the other groups' 'secret' agendas. Each party thought that after Richard III had been defeated, they would either eliminate the opposition or win them over. It was as though each group was involved in trying to play several games of chess at the same time. Everyone, however, was using the same board.

After listening to two scholarly debates on the principles of philosophy and theology at Oxford, Richard III made a generous endowment to the college. At Cotswolds he encountered Buckingham, who was returning to his estates. Charmingly, Buckingham endeared himself to the King before carrying on. At Tewkesbury Richard prayed for his brother, George. In an interesting twist of fate, George was buried in the abbey church next to Henry VI's son, the man he slayed.

The cities Richard visited offered him purses, to defray his expenses. In every case he declined. When he was able to do so, he eased the burdens of the people while his judges meted out the law with impartiality. At Worcester word was sent to the King that Maximilian was having difficulty with his Flemish subjects.

When Richard reached Warwick Castle, Queen Anne and a Spanish envoy were waiting for him. Richard signed a treaty with Spain. Before entering York, he passed through Coventry and then Leicester. Here he received word from Louis XI. "Monsieur mon cousin, I have read your letter and thank you for the news of your kingship. If I may do for you any service, I will do so eagerly for I wish to have your friendship."

Richard's single-minded opinion of the French had not altered. He sent off a terse but formal reply. "Monsieur, mon cousin, I have seen the letters you have sent me by Buckingham's herald. I understand that you want my friendship in good form and manner, which contents me well enough, for I have no intention of breaking truces signed between you and the late, noble King Edward IV, my dearly departed brother. Nevertheless, the merchants of England, seeing the great provocations your subjects have given them in seizing ships and merchandise, are fearful of venturing to Bordeaux, and other cities and ports under your rule. They need to be assured by you that they may surely and safely carry on trade, according to the rights established by the aforesaid truces. Therefore, in order that my subjects and merchants may not find themselves deceived, as a result of the ambiguity of the present situation, I pray you that by my servant, this bearer, who is one of the grooms of my stable, you will let me know in writing of your full intentions. At the same time, inform me if there is anything I may do for you, in order that I may do it with good heart. Farewell to you, Monsieur mon cousin."

In the meantime, a message arrived from the Duke of Brittany. "The French King is making violent threats of war. If you do not wish Henry Tudor delivered to Louis XI, send four thousand English archers at your expense and another two thousand at my expense. Your immediate response is requested."

The English treasury was hardly in a position to support such a venture. In addition, Richard did not wish to give credence to Henry Tudor. As his ambassador had informed him of Louis' severe ill health, Richard wrote back to the Duke to assure him that Louis XI would not be attacking anyone in the immediate future.

From Nottingham, Richard went on to Pontefract. While there he signed a treaty extending the peace with King James of Scotland. When word came that ten-year-old Prince Edward would soon be arriving, Richard hurried to finish up state business. Leaving the details to his advisors, he asked his henchmen to escort his son to his quarters as soon as he arrived.

Many felt that it was the boy's loving heart that had kept him alive. Though he was not ill, the household felt that it would be too difficult on the small boy to ride the distance from Middleham to Pontefract. He was escorted by carriage! Richard's spirits lightened as soon as he saw his son. Edward flew into the comfort of his father's arms. Richard's heart leaped in his chest. "You are growing stronger, Edward!"

On August 30th, Louis XI died in awful fear that the devil would take his soul to hell. Richard's letter arrived afterwards. Louis never had the opportunity to read it. The boy King, Charles VIII, now sat on the French throne.

On August 30th, the English royal family and their entourage made a grand state entrance into the city of York. Throngs of people gathered, the streets were adorned with banners. Trumpets and clarions announced the King and Queen. A majestic welcome greeted them.

A courier arrived from Chancellor Russell. Richard spotted the disturbed look on the messenger's face, well before he bowed. He handed Richard the sealed letter. "My Liege, the Chancellor has asked that you read this in private."

Richard excused himself. Locating a quiet place, he read the letter. Shocked, he queried the courier. "They are missing! How is it possible that Edward's sons are missing?"

"The boys must have been persuaded to leave on their own account. We found no blood! No signs of a struggle!"

"What did the boys take with them?"

"Nothing! Nothing is missing! Two young chimneysweeps were seen early in the morning. It is possible that they could have been the Princes. Chancellor Russell would like your advice."

Richard considered his options. "Say nothing! Dispatch men to search for my nephews. Send spies to determine what use the Woodvilles have planned for the Princes." Richard's mind whirled. "Send word to James Tyrell, the Master of my Henchmen, to bring cloth of gold and purple to York for my son's induction as the Prince of Wales."

Richard returned to the festivities as if nothing had happened. The splendor continued through September 8th, when young Edward was invested as Prince of Wales. The ceremony rivaled that of the King and Queen's coronation.

Before leaving the North, Richard established a royal household at Sheriff Hutton. This was also to serve as a residence for George Plantagenet's son, Edward, the Earl of Warwick. John, Earl of Lincoln, the son of Richard's sister, the Duchess of Suffolk, was to supervise. In addition, Richard began laying extensive plans for the Council of the North.

In the middle of September, Anne went with Prince Edward to Middleham with several men who were to be new members of the household; one of James Tyrell's men was included. Not long afterwards, Richard headed south. He arrived in Lincoln at the beginning of October.

Richard III had many supporters throughout the realm. In addition, too many people knew about the planned insurrection for it to be kept secret. Barely had Richard entered through

Lincoln's city gates when a courier brought news that a rebellion had broken out. Buckingham was the leader! Betrayal hit Richard with the force and suddenness of an apoplectic seizure; he saw clearly that the throne had been Buckingham's ambition from the beginning. Buckingham's offers of friendship and assistance were now seen in their true light, platitudes and discursive speeches to ensnare him into a false sense of assurance. Officially declaring Buckingham a rebel, Richard sweetened the prospects of the traitor's capture by offering a hefty guerdon.

Plans for the rebellion abruptly and without prior warning degenerated into disarray when Buckingham brought news that the princes had been savagely murdered. The report was followed immediately by Henry Tudor's generous offer to marry the Princess Elizabeth should he be crowned king. Tudor's message went on to suggest that a union of the Houses of Lancaster and York would bring an end to the War of the Roses.

The Countess of Richmond sought out the bereaved Dowager Queen. After much solace, Henry's mother offered a proposal. "Who else could have ordered this dastardly deed other than Richard? His men guarded your sons! My son, Henry Tudor, Earl of Richmond, has offered his hand in marriage to Princess Elizabeth. If you will consent, he and the Princess will rule jointly as King Ferdinand and Queen Isabella govern Spain." Elizabeth, incensed and hungry for revenge, aversely consented.

While men from the City of York were summoned to arms under the banner of the white boar, the Duke of Norfolk blocked the Woodville army's approach to London. As Richard marched south to put himself between Buckingham and the Woodville army, Henry Tudor prepared to sail. Duke Francis had provided the fleet.

199

Events had not commenced as Buckingham had hoped. Wet weather and Welsh forces from behind beleaguered him. Humphrey Stafford burned bridges and set up blockades in front of him. Buckingham's discontented men, who had been forced into harness with no desire to face the illustrious general of Gloucester, were abandoning Buckingham's cause like deer running from the dogs.

Men did not flock to any of the insurgent's causes - Buckingham, Lancastrian or Woodville's. Seeing the futility of the effort, John Morton escaped to Flanders, leaving Buckingham to hold the bag. Buckingham changed into commoner's garments before running into hiding.

The reward on Buckingham's head was too high to be ignored. Ralph Bannaster gave away Buckingham's hiding place to the Sheriff of Shropshire, who easily apprehended Buckingham. He confessed readily and then begged on his knees to speak with the King. He hoped that Richard would spare his life if he revealed the details of the Princes' deaths. However, Richard was too embittered to listen to anything Buckingham had to say. Richard stayed away! On November 2nd, a terrified Henry Stafford was beheaded in Salisbury.

Like a termagant, a storm at sea trounced and separated Henry Tudor's vessels. By the time he approached Dorset harbor of Poole, Henry Tudor was left with only two ships. On the shore men loyal to Richard feigned allegiance to Henry Tudor. They shouted out that the rebellion had been successful, encouraging Tudor to come to shore. Henry was not to be deceived; sensing danger, he sailed back to Brittany. The Marques of Dorset and the Courtenays followed suit.

Sir Thomas Saint Leger, Richard's eldest sister's second husband, and an agent for the Woodvilles, was caught, tried and executed. The Countess of Richmond's properties were given to her husband, Lord Stanley, who was rewarded further with the castle and lordship of Kymbellton. The territory and offices Buckingham once held in the Welsh Marches were distributed amongst several men, including Sir James Tyrell.

Rumors from Brittany crossed the Channel; it was said that King Richard had murdered his own nephews. Gossip fell on deaf ears. Richard III was already King when the sons of Edward IV disappeared. King Richard had no motive!

The *Croyland Chronicle* reported, "Edward and his brother were withdrawn into the inner apartments of the Tower proper. Day by day they began to se seen more rarely behind the bars and windows, till at length they ceased to appear altogether. A Strasbourg doctor, the last of his attendants whose services the King enjoyed, reported that the young King, like a victim preparing for sacrifice, sought remission of his sins by daily confession and acts of penance. He believed that death was facing him."

In London, the Richard and Anne celebrated Christmas without the Prince of Wales. He easily became ill and was better off away from court. At Rennes Cathedral in Brittany on Christmas morning, Henry Tudor swore before the exiled Lancastrians that he would marry Princess Elizabeth.

On the sea, Breton corsairs captured and plundered English merchant vessels. Richard struck back with a vengeance, vowing to bring Duke Francis to his knees for recklessly supporting pirates and harboring Henry Tudor. Lord Howard was Richard's Admiral and weapon of choice. It wasn't long before Breton ships, prizes of war, were escorted into English harbors. Breton goods in London were seized and brought to the Exchequer. To protect English merchant ships, the Royal Navy provided an escort using a convoy system Richard devised.

When the Commons met in January 1484, they elected one of Richard's good friends, William Catesby, as Speaker. Bishops Ely, Exeter and Salisbury, who had participated in the rebellion, were punished in that they were not allowed to enjoy their property. Parliament granted small parcels of lands to Lovell and Tyrell, which they had laid claim to. All of the Percy lands that had formerly been confiscated were returned.

Parliament then set about the work of radically reforming the English system of justice. Richard and his Council drafted laws that would bring equal justice to everyone. Men like William Catesby, Francis Lovell and Richard Ratcliffe served as members of the Council of the North. Learned clerics, like John Russell, added their collective input into laying down the format of law and government.

In all, six statutes were passed. The first made it unlawful for the seller of land to conceal from a purchaser that a portion of the property had already been sold to someone else. The second stated that only the court could proclaim fines, and public notice must be sent out. The third ended the practice of benevolences that Edward IV had used to extract money for war. The fourth dealt with abuses caused by extending the authority of temporary courts set up at fairs. Fair courts, henceforth, would only hear matters concerning activities at fairs for which they were set up. The fifth curbed the practice of jury packing. The sixth gave rights to those accused of crimes. Bail was allowed for those who were charged with felonies, and property could not be seized before conviction.

In addition, Richard signed statutes protecting the merchant class that had originated in the Commons. Richard understood that a strong middle class brought with it a strong economy and a strong country. He was sensitive to middle class needs, as well as their growing power.

An act protecting printing and distribution of books was passed. Livery and maintenance were to be stopped. Municipal officers were ordered that no citizen was to accept liveries or retainers. Richard's personal grants to the College of Arms turned the royal officers of arms into a corporation.

Edward IV had extended the security of justice to the lower class through a committee. Richard went a step further by creating what came to be known as the Court of Requests. Here the poor were able to have their day in court.

Richard instituted other improvements in government. The Admiralty Office was created by commission - Wode and Brackenbury with a small handful of staff kept records. The King's Household in the North at Sheriff Hutton officially became the headquarters of the Council of the North. The Council itself functioned regionally, as the Council at Westminster served the entire country. Many of the functions of the cumbersome office of the Exchequer were transferred to the Officer of the Household and the Treasurer of the Royal Chamber. This gave Richard more control over his personal finances. The matter of the Dowager Queen and the princesses was left undecided.

In a drunken moment, one of Tyrell's men let it slip to a Lancastrian loyalist the full details of the fate of the Princes. Though incensed by the horror of the crime, the man had the good sense to keep his wits about him. Later, he made his way to Westminster Abbey, where he managed to speak to the still grieving Dowager Queen. After telling her his story, Elizabeth Woodville was devastated! She recognized the man as a supporter of Henry Tudor, Earl of Richmond. It made no sense for him to tell her such a lie and go against his politics. Dispatching a letter to

Dorset, Elizabeth explained the situation. She pleaded with her son, "Abandon Henry Tudor! Return to England! Throw yourself upon the mercy of King Richard!"

Elizabeth sent word to Richard. If he would publicly swear to protect her daughters, she would release them to his care. On March 1st, Richard obliged by making a solemn public oath to protect the Princesses. The ladies left their sanctuary!

Several days later, Richard and Anne set off for Middleham to visit their son. On the way they stopped at Cambridge, where Anne made gifts of endowment and money to the University. Richard set up scholarships and granted money to King's college.

While there, he received good news. Norfolk's unrelenting pressure on Breton ships had forced the Duke of Brittany to yield. A truce was signed. To further end piracy, Richard established the Office of the Admiralty to investigate suspicious vessels or activities.

By the middle of April, the royal couple was at Nottingham, preparing at last to leave for Middleham. A courier from the North arrived before their departure. Richard knew something was terribly wrong by the grave look on the messenger's face. Grimly, Richard read the news; Edward, his beloved son, had died suddenly. Anne went white, fainting at the news. Both parents were grief stricken. The *Croyland Chronicle* reported, "You might have seen his father and mother in a state almost bordering on madness by reason of their sudden grief."

Richard and Anne reluctantly traveled to Middleham where only a funeral and memories awaited them. With his heir dead, duty required Richard to name another. He was unable to do so! He was too caught up in anguish, tempered by a streak of anger; his general's sensibilities told him that something was not quite right.

Richard III encouraged moral uprightness through example and discourses with the clergy. He was an enthusiast of the New Learning. A lover of music, he sponsored artists. He re-edified numerous palaces and castles, and provided funds for completion of both St. George's chapel and the building of the chapel at King's College. His religious experience after his father's death left him with the absolute knowing that personality survives death. He was generous in gifts, grants and gave alms to the poor. His mother's influence instilled in him a respect for women; he relieved the distress of widows and helped the wives of disenfranchised traitors. He supported his two illegitimate children and attended the marriage of his daughter, Katherine Plantagenet, to William Herbert, Earl of Huntington. As a wedding gift, he gave them one of his properties.

Richard was well thought of by his many friends and acquaintances, as well as visiting dignitaries. Nicolas von Poppelau, a German noble, had nothing good to say about the English people when he returned to the German Princes. However, of the King, von Poppelau offered a favorable summation, "Richard III has a great heart!"

What Richard was unable to deal with was his growing anger. Friends and those who had sworn oaths of allegiance had turned into conspirators. Disloyalty was compounded by the seemingly senseless losses in his personal life. Within less than two years, four male members of the House of York nearest to, or wearing the Crown, had died unexpectedly before their time. His spies had turned up no evidence of the whereabouts of his two nephews; they were assumed dead.

The Earl of Dorset was much troubled by his mother's news of Henry Tudor's involvement in the death of his half brothers. He waited for an opportune moment to flee, but Henry's men caught him in the act, forcing him to return. Henry fumed! Not long afterwards, John Morton warned Henry that Richard III had signed a treaty with Brittany. As part of the deal, Henry Tudor was to be handed over to the British. Henry escaped to the welcome arms of the French court.

Summer passed quickly! Queen Anne's melancholy regressed to dismal despair; the King pursued a punishing schedule. Richard copied Louis XI by building up an arsenal of artillery in the Tower of London, in spite of the fact that gunpowder was tricky and accidents were not uncommon. In France, Richard's spies kept track of Henry Tudor's movements. So that he might be informed immediately of any matters of importance, Richard re-instituted the system of relay riders.

Scotland, with the encouragement of France, was making military preparations against England. Additional men were added to the fortresses in the Marches. When the royal forces met the Scottish army, the English were victorious. Richard stepped up military and diplomatic pressure on James III for a permanent peace. Richard commanded the fleet he had commissioned at Scarborough, and won a decisive victory over the Scots at sea. The onslaught was too much! James III capitulated; he was ready for peace. While the treaties were being drawn up, Richard went to Pontefract to firm up the Council of the North.

In August, Richard was able to consider the matter of naming his heir apparent. George's son was mentally challenged; the blood between the Duke of Clarence and Isabel Neville ran too thin. The next in line of succession was the Earl of Lincoln, the son of his sister, Elizabeth, and the Duke of Suffolk. Richard named Lincoln the Lieutenant of Ireland and heir to the throne.

Richard returned to London. While there he attended the solemn ceremony in which Henry VI's remains were moved and entombed in St. George's Chapel. No sooner had the bones been laid to rest than Richard returned to Nottingham for the signing of the peace accord with Scotland.

With great ceremony, the Scottish ambassadors arrived for the signing of the treaty. The terms of the treaty included a provision that Richard's niece, Anne de la Pole, would marry James III's heir, the Duke of Rothesay. Among those present was Archdeacon of Lothian, James III's secretary. The Scots were generally larger in stature than the English, causing the Archdeacon to find an interesting praise for the English King, "Never had nature endowed a small frame with so great a soul and strength of mind."

In November, a traitor, who had sent statistical information to Henry Tudor, was apprehended, tried, convicted and executed. Colyngbourne had been in the service of the Duchess of York as her secretary. He was also the author of a seditious rhyme, which he had affixed to the large oak doors of St. Paul's.

> The Cat, the Rat, and Lovell our dog
> Rule all England under a Hog.

In the same month, Richard received word that Henry Tudor would be attacking the following summer. John de Vere, the former Earl of Oxford, was ordered moved from his cell in Hammes Castle in Calais to the White Tower. However, with the help of his keeper, James Blount, de Vere escaped. Richard, angered by the latest disloyalty, issued fresh commissions of array. Richard's bastard son, John of Pomfret (often called John of Gloucester), kept his appointment as Captain of Calais. James Tyrell was dispatched to Calais.

1484 was not quite over! Innocent VIII, the first pope to acknowledge his bastards, ordered the persecution of witches. Severe plagues drew Leonardo da Vinci's attention to the planning of an ideal city. King Ferdinand and Queen Isabella remained occupied with the conquest of the Moors and the forging of Spain into a nation state. Christopher Columbus sailed a stately Portuguese man-o-war to Mina on the Gold Coast of Africa. And the Red Pale was offering for sale freshly published copies of Geoffrey Chaucer's *Canterbury Tales*. The printing press had made books available to the middle class as well as the lords.

Christmas 1484 was a lavish affair. Richard outdid any Lucullian banquet Edward IV ever presented to his court. Epicurean delights and exotic viands delighted the palates of lords and ladies alike. Plays and minstrels performed throughout the day and evening. The five princesses attended all of the festivities adorned in the finest fabrics that had been created into the latest fashions.

Queen Anne was radiantly attired. However, the contrast of her fabulous gowns against the graying pallor of her skin and weak constitution was unambiguous. She was dying! As often happens between a husband and wife who have lost a child, Anne and Richard had grown further apart. The news that Henry Tudor's invasion would come in the summer only added more stress, burdening Anne's already compromised constitution. She was, however, the one who knew that Henry Tudor worried her husband as well.

Tuberculosis was consuming Anne's already frail body. When she took to her bed, the doctors warned Richard that she was contagious. He must refrain from seeing her. A total eclipse of the sun occurred on March 16, 1485; it was also the day that Anne Neville took her last breath. She slipped easily to the Otherside, where her grandfather was waiting for her. Gladly, she took his hand and stepped into the Light, eager to leave the cares of the world behind.

Bosworth Field

Henry Tudor's anxiety went through the roof when a dispatcher brought news that the Dowager Queen, Elizabeth Woodville, released all of her daughters to Richard's keeping. If Richard married them off, most of his support would vanish. Now he was being told that Queen Anne was dead. What if Richard married Princess Elizabeth? His cause would be lost!

His advisors suggested that his worries had possibilities. They would spread the rumor throughout England that Richard poisoned his Queen so that he would be free to marry Edward's daughter. This gossip, unlike the tale that Richard had murdered his nephews, took root. So much so, that Richard's closest friends advised him not to marry Elizabeth. A dozen members of the clergy informed the King that the Pope would not grant permission for a marriage so close in blood.

Livid at the personal attack on his character, Richard considered that Henry Tudor must be demonic for thinking up such an outrageous proposal. At first, he ignored the slander. It was only when public pressure forced him to make a public statement that Richard proclaimed to a waiting assemblage that marriage to Princess Elizabeth had never crossed his mind. He wrote to the Mayor of York, "Pay no heed to the evil propagators of sedition who daily sow seeds of slander against our person."

The realm was stable but the treasury was depleted. Money had been used to suppress Buckingham's rebellion, bring the Scots to the peace table and forcing Duke Francis to reconsider where his loyalties lay. Lots of money! Richard managed to collect some £20,000 to defend the realm against Tudor's invasion, which was now sponsored by the French.

The coasts were watched! Richard took up his position at Nottingham Castle. Shortly after his arrival, Lord Stanley asked if he might be permitted to leave to attend to his estates. His son, Lord Strange, would remain at Nottingham. Richard's advisors begged him not to agree to the proposition. Richard acquiesced to Stanley's request, but the King's friends made certain that Lord Strange was kept under constant watch.

Petulantly, Richard passed his time by hunting in Sherwood Forest. On August 11th, word came that Henry Tudor's forces had landed in Wales. Henry Tudor had left the Marques Dorset behind in Paris, as insurance to the French government that the money they had advanced him for the Lancastrian cause would be repaid.

Henry had set sail with a fleet of fifteen ships. Approximately 500 Englishmen and 2,000 French prisoners accompanied him. Not wishing to send good French soldiers, the French had scrapped together some of the most ruthless criminals from their jails. The prisoners were released on condition they fight for the Lancastrian cause.

Men, like John Morgan, with a small number of followers joined Henry's ranks. However, the large number of Welshmen that Henry had counted upon failed to arrive. There was no popular rising in England against King Richard. When Henry was told that Rhys ap Thomas had declared for Richard, he sent word that the office of Lieutenant of Wales was his for life if Rhys ap Thomas would join him. Henry then dispatched letters to the Stanleys and others to join him at once. Replies were noncommittal!

Henry was out of his environment. He knew nothing of war, save for the fact that the red dragon banner he marched under had been that of the great chieftain, Cadwallader. He also knew that London was the key to the kingdom. However, his advisors counseled against marching to London. It would be better not to have a general as skilled as Richard at his back. While the Stanleys were not ready to join him, they suggested that he advance towards Richard.

Richard sent word to Brackenbury, Lovell, Norfolk, Northumberland and other captains to join him. While Richard celebrated the holy feast of the Assumption of Our Lady, men were marching to his cause. Others, like John Paston and the Duke of Suffolk, who had had enough of the misfortunes and unpredictable outcomes of war, were sitting it out. Unbeknownst to Richard, Northumberland had failed to array the men of York.

Lord Stanley sent word that he had the sweating sickness and was home in bed. Lord Strange tried to escape, but was caught in the act. Fearing the worst, Lord Strange threw himself on the King's mercy. He confessed that along with Sir William Stanley and John Savage they had meant to join Henry Tudor's rebellion. Richard ordered ink and paper be brought to Lord Strange, who wrote, "Father, I am in terrible danger. Bring your forces and join the King."

On August 19th, Richard and his forces left Nottingham for Leicester. John Howard and the men who marched under his silver lion banner were also marching towards Leicester. Other men were on the road to join the King.

That same evening, Henry Tudor was having misgivings. He had remained in Lichfield with a small contingent of men while his army had marched on to Tamworth. Gathering all of the courage he could muster, Henry joined his badly shaken troops the following day. The Stanleys were still not totally committed.

On August 20th, Sir Robert Brackenbury, Constable of the Tower, arrived with men in arms from London but without the Tower's arsenal. Richard had not ordered it. Brackenbury joined Norfolk, Surrey and the other captains in a council of war. That evening, Northumberland at last arrived. Nearby, both the Stanleys and Henry Tudor were encamped.

The royal army marched on Sunday, August 21st, towards Tudor's army. Norfolk and Surrey led the vanguard, followed by Richard on a white charger. Northumberland and lords from the North and Midlands brought up the rear. Word was sent to Stanley to join the royal forces. His reply was ambiguous.

When they reached Redmore Plain, Richard set up camp on the high ground. The line faced west, effectively halting Henry's advance to London. Richard's troupes formed the left guard, Norfolk the vanguard and Northumberland the right guard. Sir William Stanley's forces were camped to the northwest, Henry's to the southwest, and Lord Stanley was to the south.

Richard met with his captains before dinner. It was decided that their armies would arise early, so as to take up the strategic position on Ambien hill. As his troops were tired, Northumberland made the suggestion that they remain hindermost in the battle position.

Restlessly, Richard checked his equipment and then walked the line of his troops. When at last Richard settled down to sleep, his dreams were disturbing. A nightmare awakened him. He rose suddenly knowing with absolute certainty that he would die on the field the following day. Unable to sleep, he waited.

Richard did not eat breakfast. John Kendall delivered a message to Stanley from Richard, requesting him to join the royal army. Stanley replied that he had other sons; he would not be joining Richard. Richard's rage blazed to the forefront. He ordered Lord Strange's execution. The King's out-of-character directive unsettled his captains. Bringing his anger under control, Richard rescinded the command.

Against his advisors' objections, Richard placed a gold diadem on his helmet. He argued, "Friends and foe will know where I am. If I fall, the battle will end quickly."

Howard's silver lion banner preceded the vanguard. Howard took up a position part way down the hill; Richard waited on top of the hill. They had succeeded in surprising Tudor! Richard called for volunteers with keen sight to serve as scouts to determine exactly which man was Henry Tudor.

Norfolk stretched his line thin, with the outer most edges of the line curving further down the hill. John Howard charged down onto Oxford's men. Norfolk's line bulged but then the outer limits of Howard's line pushed Oxford's men to the center. Oxford disengaged to regroup. Norfolk signaled his men to advance.

A scout, who had located Tudor, returned to Richard. Tudor was mounted on a black charger next to the dragon banner, surrounded by mounted troops. To get to Henry, Richard and the men of his Household would have to pass directly in front of Sir William Stanley's army, mounted under the banner of the white hart.

Bad news arrived! John Howard, Duke of Norfolk was slain, but his son, the Earl of Surrey, continued to lead the vanguard. More bad news! Northumberland refused to commit his men.

Richard mounted his white charger and closed his visor. A member of his Household handed the King his battleaxe. Starting down the hill, Richard and his Household swung north around Surrey's battle line, charging directly towards Henry Tudor.

Henry's guard advanced to meet the King. Sir John Cheyney, a giant of a man, clashed into Richard. Richard took Cheyney down with one swing of his axe. Richard's horse was down! His men pressed in around him. They heaved their way towards Tudor. Richard cut down William Brandon. The red dragon banner went down as well.

Sir William Stanley signaled his men to charge the King. One of Richard's men dismounted, offering him his horse. Richard refused! He was now in the thickest of the battle. Weapons pierced through his armor. Richard cried out in rage, "Treason! Treason! Treason!" Unable to stand, he stumbled to the ground. Still swords penetrated into him, battleaxes pounded him. In shock, Richard's body bled profusely. The pain was gone. With his last breath, Richard's soul left his battered body.

Men were marching from all parts of England to join the royal forces; however, Richard's death immediately ended the conflict. The seemingly interminable War of the Roses had at last come to an end. Sir William laid hold of the golden diadem, and crowned Henry on the battlefield.

A handful of Richard's men, including Francis Lovell and Humphrey Stafford, escaped. By remaining neutral, Northumberland was not held accountable by Henry Tudor. However, when Percy's men discovered that he had refused a direct order from Richard during the battle to advance banners, Percy's life was in imminent danger. Percy requested to be put in protective custody.

When the Earl of Surrey was brought to Henry Tudor and questioned as to his loyalties, Thomas Howard hid his anger, "My allegiance is to the crowned king of England. Were that crown on the head of a stock, I would fight for that stock. As I fought for Richard, so will I fight for you."

Henry liked Surrey's answer! As he needed talented men for his government, Thomas Howard was allowed to keep his title, but the title and lands of the Duke of Norfolk were forfeited to the crown. An extremely unpopular measure created Henry Tudor the King of England on August 20th, marking those who fought for Richard as traitors.

To a man, the citizens of York would have banded together and fought Henry Tudor, but Henry

VII had rumors circulated that the Earl of Lincoln had been slain on the field. Without a prospective king, the men of York were unable to rally. The Mayor of York and its leading citizenry issued a proclamation. "King Richard, late mercifully reigning upon us, was piteously slain and murdered, to the great heaviness of this City."

A falcon's halter was placed around the neck of the dead King. Richard's body was striped naked then thrown over the back of a horse. The corpse lay in the house of the Grey Friars for public view for two days. Afterwards, it was rolled into a grave without a marker.

Accumulative anger, which had bubbled up within Richard from the time of George's death, to the betrayal of Stanley and Northumberland at Bosworth Field, encompassed the soul of Richard III. All around him were souls of the departed. Those, like John Howard, were able to rise above the field of battle. To these men, their heavenly reward awaited as they ascended into a vortex of Light surrounded by angels. The drama they were leaving behind now seemed of small consequence.

Heaviness of rage encumbered the dead King, preventing him from moving upwards. There were other souls besides Richard, whose negative emotions bound them to the earth. There were also those who did not realize that they were dead, continuing on in a fruitless array.

In the midst of his despair, a light appeared in front of Richard. Out from which emerged a tall, glorious figure of a great knight. Richard did not recognize Edward immediately; when he did, he felt the comfort of love and joy. Edward grasped his shoulders in the familiar way. "You have done well, Richard!"

"Are you here to help me?"

"Yes, but not in the way you might have hoped!"

Edward pointed to the field of anger surrounding Richard. "You must lose this before you are able to ascend."

"How?"

"It is difficult to work out these matters in this place you find yourself. You are being given a choice to be born again."

Richard would not have believed it was possible for a soul to be born again were these words not coming from Edward. "Where?"

"In the Holy Land!"

"As a knight?"

"No, as a fig farmer!"

"A fig farmer! Why?"

Edward grinned, "So that you might walk in another's shoes. Learn what impact a conquest has on the conquered. It is the way in which a soul learns."

"Do I have a choice?"

"Yes, you always have choices."

"What are my options?"

"Spoken as a true general!" Undaunted, Edward pointed to the souls around them. "Look, there are many souls in your dilemma. Some of them are going off with an angel or escort. These particular souls will be reborn in a predicament they hated in life." Edward grinned, "Some will be born as Jews, others as women. Lancastrians will be reborn as Yorks and Yorks as Lancastrians."

Richard watched some of the souls shaking their heads. "What of them?"

"Some will take up their haunts around Henry Tudor. Others will be drawn to that which they are held most accountable for. Still others will hang about familiar abodes. This may be your choice but it will take longer, much longer for you to advance."

Richard left with Edward for the Holy Lands! It was the end of the Plantagenet rule! The thirteenth and last Plantagenet king was slain!

Power Without Love

... a dark prince and infinitely suspicious and his time full of secret conspiracies.

Francis Bacon

The monks of Scone Abbey did not intend their incantations to be in any way remotely concerned with black magic. It was a dark spell, nevertheless! The good monks had acted quickly when they learned that Edward III was on his way to claim the Stone. While the real Speaking Stone was on its way to Ireland, the monks searched for another. After a suitable red sandstone replacement had been located, the monks prayed that Edward III would not discover the deception. Then they went one step further. As the true Stone of Scone, much like the stone that held Excalibur, proclaimed the true ruler, should not the imitation do the opposite? The pretender would draw to itself its own nature. Thus, not the true king, but a false king would sit upon the English throne. It had taken many generations of kings and battles with those of consciousness to bring the curse into full realization. Now on the throne of England sat a man, more Welsh and French than English, with a thread-worn connection aligning him to Edward III through a bastard lineage. Henry's bloodlines to the mad Charles IV were stronger than those to the old English kings.

Henry VII justified his actions in obtaining the throne as a means to an end. The deaths of Edward IV, the Princes in the Tower and Prince Edward were unavoidable. Blaming Richard for his crimes was initially a shrewd political move. Not long after, he began believing his own propaganda.

Henry longed for acceptance, even love from his subjects. These were not to be his! The

217

English people were very happy with Richard III. They had no need or wish to be rescued by Henry Tudor, Earl of Richmond.

Though he had sworn to marry Princess Elizabeth if he became king, Henry postponed the ceremony until after his coronation. He was determined to show England, as well as all of Europe, that he ruled on his own claim to the throne. Robert Dymmock served as Henry VII's champion, as he had done for Richard III. Robert Dymmock was one of only a few lords and gentry who bothered to show up for the pompous coronation.

Henry's other reason for hesitating to marry Princess Elizabeth was that he had been advised that Edward IV's children were illegitimate. However, if he didn't marry Elizabeth much of his support would leave. In addition, he had given a public oath! It would look bad if he reneged!

Henry then sent retainers out to destroy any and all evidence of Edward IV's precontract to Lady Eleanor Butler. The Parliamentary records declaring Edward's children illegitimate were wiped out. The Bishop of Bath and Wells was permanently stopped from repeating the tale of Edward IV's first marriage. Henry and his closest advisors rampaged through Richard's private papers, obliterating any evidence the Bishop had provided Richard. In addition, they burned anything that might speak of the dead King's humanity, hoping to raze their own guilt as well.

Elizabeth Woodville had told her daughters that Henry Tudor had been responsible for their brothers' deaths. Though Princess Elizabeth had no desire to marry Henry Tudor, she was also left without choice. After Elizabeth's coronation on January 18, 1486, she was kept a virtual prisoner, bearing her plight bravely. Henry knew that it was his Queen whom the people loved. It only served to arouse his envy, distancing himself further from his wife and the people. Henry found a single,

218

redeeming quality in Elizabeth; Prince Arthur was born at Winchester on September 30, 1486.

Margaret Beaufort reigned as Queen by her son's side. Taking a vow of chastity after Bosworth Field, Margaret left her husband, Lord Stanley, to his own devises. Thomas Stanley was rewarded for his service with the earldom of Derby, but he had more power under Richard III. Lord Stanley's claim to fame under the Tudor reign was 'husband of the King's mother'.

Henry VII took credit for innovations in government and law, which Edward IV and Richard III had established. He then used the machinery of government and law to rule England as a conquering dictator. He did not, however, take retribution against the English on behalf of Wales as he had promised his Welsh supporters. Instead, Henry set about to annex Wales. Rhys ap Thomas was not made Lieutenant of Wales! The Welsh were not alone in regretting their failure to support Richard III, nor were they the only ones Henry Tudor broke his promise to. The people of Wales, however, were the angriest!

Henry VII was a fairly good-looking man until he spoke, revealing a set of black teeth. He aged prematurely, becoming an old man before his time. His doctors were unable to help him. He did have his good points; he supported poets and minstrels. He was well read, and encouraged learning and the arts.

Henry was a master of finance but his miserliness impeded his soul's growth. He was only interested in ventures, political or personal that yielded a profit. Money was his motto!

He taxed his subjects heavily. When word was brought of complaints, he ordered those individuals who whined to be taxed all the more. Henry VII's agents, Dudley and Empson, ruthlessly extorted fines and taxes. After Henry VII died,

Henry VIII inherited a treasury of £1,500,000 that had been literally extracted from the English people. Dudley and Empson were so unpopular that as one of his first acts as king, Henry VIII was compelled to have the pair beheaded.

Edward IV and Richard III had been accessible and concerned; Henry VI was loved for his benevolence. Henry VII was the antithesis of his three predecessors, and with his advisors he ran a secretive government. Henry VII was so hated that commoners and foreign royalty, alike, backed pretenders to the throne. While Henry VII was able to quell these insurrections after considerable effort, what bothered him the most was the support that blatant commoners were able to amass to their cause.

In 1485, Lambert Simnel, the son of an Oxford tradesman, announced that he was the son of the Duke of Clarence. Henry had the real Earl of Warwick brought out from the Tower and put on display. People still supported the pretender!

Henry suspected the Dowager Queen Elizabeth of coaching Simnel. Though the old Queen was his mother-in-law, she was relieved of what little property Henry had allowed her to keep and immured in the convent of Bermondsey. It was perilous for anyone to attempt to contact or see her.

In 1489, the citizens of York were presented with the opportunity to adequately demonstrate their displeasure to the Earl of Northumberland. Henry Percy reluctantly rode into the city on an errand for the King. His most trusted, well-armed men surrounded him; however, when the mob attacked the Earl, his guards stepped aside. With Percy's death, Henry VII reinstituted Richard's Council of the North, claiming it as his own inventiveness.

William Stanley had been given lands and received the appointment of Lord Chamberlain.

However, he was granted no title. Henry reasoned that William Stanley had tarried too long before committing himself at Bosworth; thus, endangering his life - the life of the King.

In 1491, there was a new pretender; this one claimed to be Prince Richard, Edward IV's youngest son. His real name was Perkin Warbeck. Like Lambert Simnel, Perkin Warbeck also won support from both the people and foreign monarchs.

In January 1495, Sir William Stanley was charged with treasonous conduct. On February 5th, he was beheaded. The evidence against William Stanley was that he was overheard to say, "If Perkin Warbeck is indeed the son of Edward IV, I will never fight against him."

Neither the City of York nor anyone else could bring Richard III back. The Earl of Lincoln had disappeared after an attempt to overthrow King Henry. When Cecile died in 1495, the Royal House of York came to an end. She was buried next to her husband.

In the same year, the ambassador from Milan wrote back to Italy. "Henry VII is rather feared than loved. This is due to his avarice. He is powerful and rich, but if fortune allowed some lord of royal blood to rise and the King had to take the field, he would fare badly owing to his greed. His people would abandon him."

The following year, the Spanish ambassador wrote to King Ferdinand and Queen Isabella. "The decrease in trade between our country and England may be attributed to the impoverishment of the English people. Great taxes are laid upon them. The King himself informed me that he intentionally keeps his subjects low; sincerely believing that riches would only make them haughty. While the King is widely disliked, the Queen is beloved because she is powerless like them. The people love Prince Arthur, as he is the grandchild of

King Edward. Henry VII would like to govern England in the French fashion but that much power and support he lacks. Those who have received the most from him are also the most discontented. The King desires to be highly spoken of throughout the world. He fails utterly, for he is not a great man."

Lies have neither weight nor substance. Lies require additional lies until the tale becomes complicated, even illogical. In this manner, Richard III was created into an infamous monster, who had murdered his kin to become king.

Henry VII had arrived at the point where he believed the fabrications of his historians. Uncomfortable reality returned swiftly when Thomas More made public the last confession he had heard from James Tyrell. Tyrell had been tried and condemned on trumped up charges. In his last confession, Tyrell admitted to More that he had ordered his men to murder the Princes in the Tower for the King. He went on to say that the bodies were buried at the staircase outside the White Tower. James Tyrell meant King Henry but Thomas More assumed he meant King Richard; James Tyrell meant within the stairwell but Thomas More assumed he meant the foot of the stairs. Infuriated that the issue had again come up, Henry ordered that contrary to tradition, James Tyrell was not to be allowed to make a public confession before his execution on May 2, 1502.

What to do about the bones was another matter entirely. Options were limited! Henry contemplated! If he ordered the foot of the stairs to be dug up, the bones would not be found. It would look as if Richard Plantagenet were innocent. If he had the stairs excavated people would wonder how he knew the bones were there.

What had Tyrell been thinking? Henry wanted no part of black magic; he even feared the bones. Best to let the matter blow over. If people had idle time on their hands for gossip, he would simply raise their taxes.

The infant Prince Edmund had died in 1500; in 1502, Arthur, Prince of Wales, drew his last breath at Lambert Castle. This left Henry, Prince of York, next in line to the throne. The King never liked his son, Henry. Neither the King nor anyone else, for that matter, rationally understood why. However, it was the part of Henry VII's mind that was not conscious, which recognized Henry as a reincarnation of George Plantagenet, Duke of Clarence.

It was when Elizabeth Plantagenet arrived at the royal apartments in the Tower of London before her coronation that George's soul found her under heavy guard. Laughing, he easily walked past the Yeomen. George admired her beauty of spirit, but when a light appeared next to her it startled him! A great knight stepped forth. When George realized that it was his brother, Edward, George recoiled. Edward's voice comforted him. "I am not here to do you harm. You wanted to be king? You now have your chance! The way is open for you to leave with Elizabeth. How you become king has been predetermined. What kind of a king you become is up to you."

Hate draws to itself, just as love seeks its own kind. Henry VII drew to himself that which he despised, a son of York, the Duke of Clarence. George Plantagenet's last thoughts and fervent desire to be king also drew his soul to Elizabeth and Henry.

Henry VII was devastated at the prospect of his second son, Henry, ascending to the crown. Henry talked Elizabeth into trying to have another son. Elizabeth died in childbirth the following year; the baby did not survive.

No one cried when Henry VII died in 1509. Henry's black soul did not reincarnate as another king, or even with the potential to be mayor. The anger and resentment surrounding his deeds drew Henry's soul in different directions. However, it was in Wales where Henry VII was held most accountable. Henry VII reincarnated as a poor Welsh farmer, who begrudgingly tilled Crown lands for a pittance. He, of course, hated Henry VIII and had no use for the English or their monarchy.

It was Henry VII, who trumped up charges against the Duke of Clarence's mentally challenged son and had him executed. It was Henry VIII, who executed Clarence's daughter, the Earl of Suffolk, the Marques of Exeter and many others. Henry VIII's reign began, as a promise of hope. Within a short time, his name became a byword for tyranny. One estimate put the number of people executed in the reign of Henry VIII at 70,000. Henry VIII died on January 28th, his father's birthday. The ill omen signaled the end of the House of Tudor.

The Tudor dynasty ran its course after Elizabeth I died childless. Soon afterwards, writers began questioning Tudor historians. William Cornwaleys' *The Encomium of Richard III* referred to Richard as a defamed King. Sir George Buc, whose ancestors fought for Richard III at Bosworth, questioned the contradictions and misinformation in the works of Vergil and More.

In 1674, a stone staircase outside the White Tower was demolished. The workmen discovered a wooden chest beneath the foundation of the stairs. Inside were the bones of two boys, who were about the ages of twelve and ten when they died. They were assumed to be the bones of the Princes in the Tower. With sufficient ceremony, the bones were placed in an urn in Westminster Abbey and laid to rest near Henry VII's tomb.

Part II

Questions & Answers

This is not the first book to suggest that someone other than Richard III murdered the princes. Previous writers, as early as Sir George Buc, suspected that the Tudor historians had gone overboard in their condemnation of Richard. Polydore Vergil and Thomas More's facts were inconsistent. Other writers, such as, John Rous, were improbable. It was Rous who said that Richard was born to the Duchess of York with hair down to his waist and a full set of teeth, after she had been pregnant for two years. These same Tudor historians attributed near saint-like qualities to the tyrant, Henry VII.

If only one part of a document is proven fraudulent, the authenticity of the entire record is questionable. It is the incongruity and implausibility within Tudor records that has caused historians and writers to question. Did Richard III murder the princes? If not, who did?

Richard III by William Shakespeare is one of the most seething portrayals of the thirteenth and last Plantagenet king. It is a difficult play, not only because of complex relationships between multiple characters, but it is confusing as well. The character of Richard III is portrayed as a clear-cut monster without pangs of consciousness. He is very unlike Shakespeare's juicy, complex characters, struggling with contradictions. This is not the only inconsistency within Richard III. The lead character wholly lacks motive for his horrific deeds. Why would Richard murder the princes when he was already king and more importantly, recognized and accepted as the ruler?

225

Shakespeare's Richard III does not operate within known historical facts. One of many examples would be that Shakespeare's Richard has assassins murder the Duke of Clarence in his prison cell while King Edward is bedridden. Edward was not ill at the time! It was Edward, who convened the peers to judge the Duke of Clarence, who was without doubt guilty of treason! Edward was the one who signed the Duke of Clarence's death warrant! George was executed, not murdered!

In the play Richard tells the audience what he is going to do and then he does it. On one such occasion, he says that he is going to wed the Lady Anne but he will see to her demise. Why go to all the bother to marry the landless daughter of a dead traitor, give up property and title to do it, and then have her murdered?

Then there is Richard's famous line in the final act, "A horse, a horse, my kingdom for a horse!" Documented statements from those on both sides of the conflict, who were actually present at the Battle of Bosworth Field, state that Richard stood his ground and died bravely.

The play is too complicated and does not work. The truth is always clear and simple, not muddy and convoluted. In all of these respects, Shakespeare's Richard III is so different from his other works, one wonders if something else is going on. Did Shakespeare know the truth about Richard III? There were still people alive during the reigns of Henry VII and Henry VIII who did know the facts. Was Shakespeare writing out of political obligation to prop up the Tudor's weak claim upon the throne? Or was it to placate the vanity of Queen Elizabeth I? Was Shakespeare's rancorous distortion of the truth intentionally woven within beautiful iambic pentameter verses to bring pause, to cause his audience to think?

Many people who have seen or read Richard III become sympathetic and even ardent supporters of the dead king. Richard becomes viewed as the much-maligned king! Richard III died over five hundred years ago. He may be the only dead monarch who has fan clubs in the form of modern Richard III societies, associations and foundations around the world.

Richard III: White Boar had its beginnings in a few short paragraphs, which gave the background of Henry VII and the Tudors in Between Two Worlds: The Story of Henry VIII and Anne Boleyn — and Her Celtic Heritage. As I was doing the research for those paragraphs what struck me as very strange was the fact that five male Plantagenets, who were either kings or in line to the throne, died within a little over two years of one another. Given that only Richard died in battle and none died from the Black Plague, these were improbable odds, even for Medieval Times! Yet, the Shakespearean version of how the evil uncle murdered the Princes, and later received his just reward at Bosworth Field remained in Between Two Worlds.

Before departing for England in the fall of 2003, Between Two Worlds, with the exception of my questions concerning Richard III, was completed. I chose to wait until I returned from England before sending it off to the printer, thinking I might find answers there. This is the account of that trip to England that I gave in the second half of Between Two Worlds:

. . . Marie Scott from Coventry mentioned in a Shamanic class, "I always keep my nose out of other people's business. In another lifetime I saw something that I should not have seen, men putting two young boys on a boat. They put out my eyes before cutting off my head."

In my third eye I could see what Marie was describing and immediately got that the boys were the two young princes being taken from the Tower.

"Edward IV's sons were not killed in the Tower of London they were murdered elsewhere!"

Marie was surprised. She said, "Exactly, Richard had nothing to gain from his nephews' deaths! Henry had everything to gain!"

Marie was my partner for the Shamanic Soul Retrieval. When I went into the Underworld to find her soul fragment there was a large white animal traveling next to me. For some time, we followed a beam of light to find that it was radiating around the edge of a large black circle. "Where are we?" I asked.

"In the eye of the witness!" Came the answer.

Abruptly before us, appeared the tortured remains of the man who had had his eyes put out. The white animal was White Boar; Richard III was assisting in Marie's healing. Before returning Richard gave me a message to give to Marie, "You volunteered to be a witness to the truth!"

Marie had felt shifts while I was in the Underworld, and cried when she heard the message. George Bogg was Marie's partner for the Shamanic Healing. After he finished describing what he had seen in the Underworld, we all felt that the same past life had been worked upon further. The droning of the Shamanic drum harmonizes the left and right brains so that imagery is seen with more clarity. So, when George retold what had happened in the Otherworlds, we were also able to see the events transpiring in our own inner eyes.

Marie felt that I needed to go to Bosworth Field. Terry Hedge took me there. We did a Hosanna clearing, opened the vortex and sent earthbound souls to the Light with the angels. Then a message came with alacrity. Richard was a soldier in an age when chivalry and a code of honor were extremely important and well valued. Richard would never have cut down innocent children. As evidenced by his reign, Henry VII lacked these scruples. While did not kill the boys himself, he certainly had made it clear that if the princes were out of the way his road to the throne would be easier. Henry VII's reign began with evil; it was doomed from its inception! Henry VIII's death on his father's birthday was an ill omen signaling the end of the Tudor dynasty.

In the afterlife, it was Richard who was the strongest of the three and it was time to clear his name. His spirit followed me back to London, where I told Brenda what had happened. Brenda Davies' received a strong confirmation that Richard was with us; she was also able to communicate with Richard. He conveyed to her that he had had a lifetime as a gardener after Richard III where he was very angry. Brenda said, "Figs! I think he was a gardener in the Middle East!"

Inner knowing came in through the top of my head, filling me with the knowledge that Richard III's support of the Crusades ensured that his next lifetime would be spent in the Holy Lands as a victim of the Crusaders. While the Crusades were nothing more than an attempt by the Church to seize lands, the populace and knights were given more heroic reasons and religious justification for terrorism. Some of the most diabolical deeds committed on this planet have been done with good intentions, in the name of God. Brenda continued, "I think that he has been trying to let go of his anger for some time."

After energizing HARTH and SEY HEY KEY, I sent them to Richard and his lifetime as a gardener. I asked the angels, "Multiply these symbols times infinity to the twenty-first power, for as many times and places as necessary. So as you heal Richard, so heal other earthbound spirits." Richard was long ready to receive the healing. "Richard release your anger to God and ask God to make matters right."

Brenda said, "He has his wings! He's flying!" Gratifying! "Richard is a really nice man! He deserves this." Brenda tuned in,

"Richard's healing will have profound effects on many people he knew then and will have ramifications now!"

Several days later, Henry VII's brown earthbound spirit appeared, looking for healing. He wanted us to know that he never wanted to be king. Rather, it was his mother and events that led him on a course his soul had never intended. He also had another lifetime that was keeping him bound to the earth plane. It was a lifetime in France before Henry VII where he murdered his wayward wife and her lover. We sent him love. After he had soaked up the energy, he was able to look somewhat at the role he had played. After asking the angels to open the vortex, Henry went to the Light. When I asked if any other earthbound spirits wanted to make their transition, many souls from Henry VII's life came into the vortex. They had been waiting to be included. Amongst these souls were the souls of more modern men and women, who had been entrapped by their own greed, anger, fear, sorrow, hatred or jealousy. The angels filled the void of their passing with energy of love, joy, compassion, abundance, truth, justice, mercy and grace. By including mercy, grace and compassion when asking for justice, then mercy, grace and compassion will come to those who ask when justice is at hand.

The death of the two young princes has been a mystery because none of the possible murder suspects 'pan out'. In 1502, Henry VII had Sir James Tyrell beheaded. Thomas More heard his last confession. Afterwards, More publicly stated that Richard III was responsible for the deaths of Edward IV's sons. Tyrell not only confessed to the murders, but he knew where the boys were buried. What may well have happened is that Tyrell stated that he had carried the carnal acts out for the King. Thomas More assumed that he meant Richard III; Tyrell actually was referring to Henry VII.

230

Tyrell was executed because he knew too much. He was a loose end; too dangerous to have around! In a robbery the police follow the money; in the princes' murder by following the power the prime suspect is Henry VII. Like Henry II, Henry VII let it be known that it would serve him well to be rid of those who stood in his way.

People in the past have looked at the possibility of Henry VII murdering the princes. However, they assume that if Henry did it, the murders were executed after he became king. However, if Richard was concerned about his nephews and hid the boys to keep them out of harms way, he would have secured his son as well! Why couldn't one of Henry Tudor's spies; such as, Tyrell, murdered the boys before Henry Tudor's invasion? Certainly, no one can deny that the demise of the two Princes made it a lot easier for Henry Tudor to assume the throne! A lot easier!

Between Two Worlds discusses sites I visited before the publication of the book in December 2003. In the spring of 2004, I returned to England, ending up in Carlisle. Carlisle Castle is very much intact; the energy one is able to feel is almost exclusively military! Our guide, Jim Anderson, was available through the English Heritage and Open Book Visitor Guides. He provided priceless information for Richard III: White Boar.

The strongest energy and psychic sensation in Carlisle Castle proved to be in the dark dungeon located in the lowest level of the castle. I did not even want to step into the dark, underground room! The feeling was that of horror and torment. This was hell!

Jim Anderson told us that Carlisle's dungeon had been on television. On the program they showed the licking stone where prisoners licked the moisture from a particularly damp stone in an effort to quench their thirst. Detainees were often forgotten in Medieval Times.

After the tour, Angela Stevens and I went back to release the trapped souls from the prison cell. Anyone who is channeling healing energy may do soul rescue. Saints angels and spirit guides are able to help us from the Otherworlds. So too, we are able to help trapped souls from this physical world. Both forms of healing and help are possible because God is limitless.

Angela and I asked the angels to open the vortex, which is like the tunnel of Light described by those who have had a near-death experience. We then invited the lost souls to step into the Light. Sometimes, more is required. There are several specific healing techniques in my other books for those who are interested.

Angela Stevens and I also went to Middleham Castle, which is now an open-air facility. I don't often see other dimensions with my physical eyes. When I do, it is important. We were on the ground floor when I was impelled to spin around and look up. On the third level was a large, black form moving quickly along the far wall. At one time, the pathway the ghost took would have been a corridor. Before disappearing through an archway, he turned to look directly at me. Instinctively, I knew that it was Warwick! Angela didn't see the black form, but she felt the presence of acute evil.

Earthbound spirits, who have been held back by heavy emotions or thoughts, are typically brown with human features. Coal black spirits do not have human characteristics. These are lost souls, who in their lifetime were literally swept away by evil, heavy thoughts or deeds; such as, murder, greed, or thirst for power and domination by any means. They may have used black magic!

The black magician stands in the middle of a pentagram - not because the pentagram is evil, but rather because it is a symbol of protection. This protection is from the demons the black magician summons to carry out the black magic. However, a symbol is only able to do so much. The demons actually begin to attach to the black magician from the first time they are called in. When the black magician dies, there is no pentagram, only demons! These demons may remain attached to the magician for lifetimes until they are released.

It was Warwick's insatiable gluttony for supremacy acted out with voracity and without concern for the consequence that held him back after his death. It was far easier to send the souls of the prisoners in Carlisle Castle to the Light or heaven than it was to assist Warwick's transition! During the clearing, energy came in to fill Middleham's great keep. Other souls, even souls of black magicians came into the vortex, took the hand of an angle and went to the Light. Along with them, many demons that had been beckoned for ill-gotten purposes went as well. Warwick's soul proved to be extremely dense; the angels worked exceptionally hard. Warwick's consciousness was eventually elevated somewhat. He allowed some measure of love to enter his being. Exhausted, neither one of us was inspired to climb to the second story for a view of the Wensleydale countryside.

Leaving the castle, we noticed a white statue of Richard III that we had not seen before. Granted, it had rained earlier that morning, but most of the water had dried up. In the corner of the statue's eyes were drops of water, as if Richard's soul was crying. Was it for joy because his friend had been willing to accept some healing? Was it in sadness because Warwick had not chosen to go to the Light? Was it a bit of both?

Afterwards, we went to lunch in the town. The owner of the restaurant/bar/hotel told us that the back wall of the tavern used to be part of the castle wall. She went on to say that many people had seen the ghost of a man riding a white horse. People assumed that it was the spirit of Richard III. When the malevolent ghost appeared in her inn, the temperature went ice cold! One individual was found stone dead on the stairs. Continuing on, she said that occupants of other buildings along the same wall had had similar difficulties.

When Henry VII's spirit came to Brenda and myself, he was brown, not black. There was a strong feeling that Henry VII had worked out a good deal of his karma through many lifetimes since his incarnation as the English king. This had been accomplished with great difficulty. There was also a feeling that someone or some event had brought his karma back to him more quickly than usual. When I asked, "Why?" the strongest impression that came to me was that the event that spurred his karma along occurred when the bones of the Princes were placed in an urn in Westminster near the tomb of Henry VII.

What happened to the soul of George, the Duke of Clarence, and later, Henry VIII? What follows is the account in *Part II* of <u>Between Two Worlds</u> in the chapter, *Canterbury Tales*:

Returning to England yet again, I stayed with Brenda and her family. Canterbury was the first stop on our list. The great majority of the people on my flight over to London had gone onto other countries; hoof and mouth disease kept many tourists away from Britain that year. Arriving at Canterbury, we had our choice of parking and the Cathedral itself was all but empty.
Canterbury Cathedral had been a shrine for pilgrims from all over Europe. On December 29, 1170, four knights on the order of Henry II murdered Thomas Becket in his cathedral. All of Christendom was outraged and under pressure from Rome, Henry was flogged at Becket's tomb on July

234

7, 1174. Both December 29th and July 7th became holy days in England.

After Becket's death there were people who visited his shrine who received healings; although more healings were recorded when Thomas Becket's body was in the crypt than after it was moved up to the main body of the Cathedral. With recorded accounts of miracles, Rome designated Becket as Saint Thomas of Canterbury. Those seeking health or other help left donations behind that ranged from pennies to precious jewels.

Henry VIII saved the suppression of the shrine of Saint Thomas in Canterbury Cathedral for last. After closing the shrine in September 1538, Henry had Becket's bones and other relics, which included the saint's hair shirt, broken skull and the sword that had split his skull, removed. Henry then appropriated some twenty or more cartloads of treasure that had been left by pilgrims for over three hundred years. People everywhere were infuriated with the monumental proportions of Henry's sacrilegious act! Anne was lucky she was not around to take the blame.

We found the site where Saint Thomas Becket had been murdered. There was definitely energy! However, after eight hundred years of visitors and pilgrims, each of whom had their own feelings about the homicide, the original carnal act was masked with many emotions and thoughts. Perhaps, reincarnations of those who had been involved in the drama would pick up specifics of the deed itself. Brenda and I headed for the crypt!

In the lower level are eight pillars and the energy is mixed. Brenda was unable to remember where the black shadow was and she walked past the second pillar and me. As she headed off, I looked up and saw the shadow on the pillar and asked Brenda, "Is this what you are looking for?"

Brenda turned and looked at me. Her mouth dropped open! "You look horrified!"

235

I was surprised at her remark because I really wasn't feeling much other than curiosity. Perhaps, it was the reaction of my subconscious. I pointed to the pillar! Brenda stepped back to look at it and then nearly jumped out of her skin! It was the trapped soul of Henry looking for release.

As Brenda held the energy, I did the Hosanna clearing as I had done at Hever Castle, and asked the angels to open the vortex as I had done for Thomas Boleyn. As the vortex opened, other lost souls were clamoring to be included, and so I asked that if they so wished to make their transition to the Light that they take the hand of an angel as well. What might be described as an etheric mob scene was created as earthbound and dark spirits hurried to the Light. It was an arduous task for the angels to release Henry from his self-imposed bondage and thus, difficult for me to stop the clearing as the occasional tourist walked by. "Oh well, these people will never see me again!" and I continued on.

Just as I was thinking that we needed help, amazingly, the Cathedral intercom came on, asking people to stop what they were doing and pray. As we all said the Lord's Prayer together, Henry's soul began to move away from the pillar and then upwards. As Henry left for the Light with the angels, the eyes of the shadow figure on the pillar looked upwards as well. Somehow, all of us had agreed on another level of consciousness to be at Canterbury Cathedral on this particular day to help the souls of Henry and the others go to the Light!

To continue with other questions of why or how the story of Richard III: White Boar evolved: What about the Tudor portrayal of Richard III as a frail and weak man? It does not hold up to the verifiable documentation that remains! At the

236

Battle of Barnet, Richard climbed up a steep, high slope to a plateau in a full set of armor. Afterwards, he engaged in vigorous hand-to-hand combat for, at the very least, two hours. Reading through the various accounts of that battle, there was no room for slackers in Edward's army, especially those in the right flank commanded by Richard Plantagenet. They could not spare a man to guard a physically challenged general. Generals and leaders were expected to fight cheek and jowl with the men-at-arms. Perhaps, if this were still true today, there would be fewer armed conflicts!

Getting back to Richard. If he were so frail, Edward never would have entrusted him with the responsibility of the position of Constable of England or commander of the critical vanguard. At Bosworth Field, the first enemy soldier Richard killed was John Cheyney, a giant of a man. By all accounts he did this alone. Is this a fragile, scrawny, weak man?

My horse, Buckley, is a tall, thin Saddlebred. However, many warm bloods are bigger; they are taller and have more muscle mass. Buckley's frame belies his strength and power; he commands attention and respect! He is one of those horses who have a core of power. He is a lot of horse; he makes working on the aids and canter pirouettes executed with vigor look easy. Yes, it takes a certain physic for a horse to be able to do dressage, run fast or race around barrels. Each of these physical endeavors requires a different psychic, just as basketball players, football players, swimmers, etc. have different physics. However, physical confirmation is only a part of it. What is found within the spirit is a bigger factor. Look at the small Seabiscuit! He had a great heart and determination. This intangible, elusive quality may be found within people as well as horses. The facts suggest that

Richard III had this quality. He was a strong, vigorous, courageous fighter in battle!

Why would biased Tudor historians say that Richard III was a hunchback? In the Middle Ages physical abnormalities were seen as a reflection of character flaws! There is no evidence whatsoever that Richard was a hunchback, aside from the mind's of Tudor historians! Because of fifteenth century prejudice, Richard never would have been accepted as a general or a king!

There are some modern historians who believe that Richard III was guilty of murdering his nephews. One example that one historian points to as evidence of Richard's weak moral fiber is the fact that Richard had two bastard children. In the Middle Ages, it was not considered a character flaw for a young bachelor to have illegitimate children.

Henry VIII also had a bastard son, whom he openly recognized and supported. While Henry VIII may not be the best choice to hold up as a role model, it does show that bastards were accepted. What was considered chivalrous was for such a man to acknowledge and provide for his bastard children, which Richard did.

Other historians, who believe in Richard III's culpability, point to the fact that he exhibited evenhandedness, compassion, justice and other admirable characteristics during his reign. Therefore, they believe that Richard's humanity is proof of his remorse for assassinating the princes. Because he was guilty, he was kind. This is illogical to the point of absurdity! First, the Duke of Gloucester was loved and respected in the North because of his integrity, love of justice and fairness before he was king. Secondly, people stay within character; rarely do people act out of character! Richard was the same man before and after he was crowned king.

It was Henry VII, who was the unpopular, harsh, unyielding tyrant throughout his reign. It was Henry VII, who betrayed his Welsh constituency. It was Henry VII who overtaxed the English. It was the Tudors who mastered the art of torture, casting a dark ominous shadow on the Tower of London that remains to this day!

No one rushed out in support of Henry Tudor when he landed on English soil. Certainly, an abused population in the hands of an evil despot, who murdered two innocent boys, would have. When news arrived that Henry VII had won the Battle of Bosworth, people were shocked, not overjoyed! Few of the nobility bothered to show up for Henry VII's coronation. Commoners and even foreign monarchs supported pretenders, who aspired to the English throne! Henry VII earned his disrespect, just as the later ghost of Marley wrought his chain of desolation through stealthy deeds.

Buckingham knew the truth about the demise of the children! He was the first one who brought the news that the Princes had been brutally slaughtered. His news came shortly after the last sighting of the Princes. How did Buckingham know the Princes were dead unless he had some hand in the deed?

Richard put his life on the line, time and again for Edward IV. He would have done the same for Edward's sons, had they been legitimate heirs to the crown, regardless of the circumstances. Richard accepted the crown by the fact that it was his by right. Secondary reasons included the fact that Prince Edward was not an adult. England was in a particularly precarious position; she would not have survived a minority rule without grave consequences.

Why do I believe that Richard III was a handsome man? Sometimes, I see Richard psychically. The English standard of beauty at the time consisted of blond hair and blue eyes. A foreigner's account of Richard III that survives stated that Richard was handsome.

Let's not forget Holbein's painting of Sir Thomas More and his family! Every object and every person in a Holbein painting has meaning for the people in the painting. When the family portrait was completed, it was said that the Duke of York was painted to the far right in the back row.

People would have still been alive, who knew or had seen the Duke of York or Richard III. These particular people considered the likeness of this non-family member to be that of the Duke of York. Rumors were whispered that Richard, Duke of York, had actually endured into Henry's VIII's reign under the protection of More. It is highly unlikely that the Duke would have chosen obscurity while Edward fought for and the ruled England.

The pleasing portrait of the Duke is, however, interesting. Records consistently state that Richard III looked very much like his father. Even the Tudor historians never claimed that Richard was a bastard; no one would have believed them! If the man in Holbein's painting is the Duke of York and Richard looked like his father, then Richard must have been good looking as well.

To digress back to Holbein for a moment! Hans Holbein was an Early Renaissance portrait painter, who delighted in detail. He was blessed with a singular capacity for expressing characterization. Why then did Holbein include a portrait of Richard of York in a group family portrait of the Mores? Or could the man in the back row be a portrait of Richard III? Did Holbein incorporate Richard III in the portrait as an attempt at humor because of the uproar created when More disclosed Tyrell's last confession? Did Holbein think that he would paint it out later? Is it possible that Thomas More did not recognize the out of place intruder because of his weak eyesight? Was it that More's family was afraid to tell the austere Thomas More, knowing that he would not find the inclusion humorous?

Why do I believe that George, Duke of Clarence, blackmailed Edward? Something quickly went wrong between the two brothers well before George joined up with Warwick! Initially, Edward went out of his way to be fair to both brothers. Edward even honored George before Richard, as George was older than Richard.

Unexpectedly and unexplainably, Edward blatantly favored Richard. In some instances, Edward seemingly went out of his way to do so. When I asked, "Why?" the answer I received was that George blackmailed Edward. When I asked psychics, who have no knowledge or bias about 15th century English history, they come up with the same answer.

Edward never told Richard. He did not wish to diminish himself in any way in his youngest brother's eyes. After seeing the calamity Clarence caused, Cecily never discussed the matter with Richard.

What is interesting about Spiritual Law is that when a possibility does not work out in one lifetime, it will in another. Edward IV had the charisma and leadership abilities to be king; George Plantagenet did not. The seed that Cecily planted in George's mind was there to help Clarence create his next lifetime as king of England. Regardless of whether or not you believe in reincarnation, the idea is intriguing, nay, generously loving, that God gives us more than one opportunity to 'get it right!' However, it is only a comforting idea, tossed about in the mind, until an individual has an experience transcending logic, whereby he or she knows for certain that he or she has lived before. There are many, many people who have had such experiences. Reincarnation: The Phoenix Fire Mystery speaks of

241

people throughout history who had such experiences and believed in reincarnation.

How is it possible for one lifetime to influence the following? While individuals in the 15th century were totally unaware of quantum physics and the field of possibilities, it was there just the same. George Plantagenet lived his days with the knowledge that he was the rightful heir to the throne. It was probably on his mind the day he died - how unjust that the rightful king was executed while the pretender sat on the throne! By his numerous attempts to claim the crown, it is obvious that George dwelled on becoming king. When George pondered, he was creating in the field of possibilities.

What came to me very strongly while writing this book is that Clarence came back as Henry Tudor, who later became Henry VIII. No one, who lived at the time, understood why Henry VII did not like his second son! Henry VII was not consciously aware of the truth. It was his subconscious that recognized his second son as a reincarnation of the son of the Duke of York.

The Creator brings universal jokes into reality when we take ourselves too seriously. Jewish tradition believes that we incarnate through family or group lineages. This is sometimes true because we are drawn to what we love. However, it is equally true that hatred, anger, sorrow or any negative emotion will draw a soul inexorably toward the individual or group that these intense feelings are directed at. In addition, the soul yearns for new experiences and looks for avenues with which to explore other possibilities.

What the #$*! Do We Know, a documentary film, may be described in one sentence as quantum physics explanation of God, and how we impact and alter our environment with our thoughts and emotions. What we dwell, worry, meditate or ponder upon with concentrated, focused awareness is what we create! This creative ability increases when we think outside of ourselves. An example of thinking inside is when we are engaged in a conversation but when the other person is talking, we are thinking about our reply. When we are listening to what is being said, we are thinking outside of ourselves.

A concrete example of how our minds create is the sequence in <u>What the #$*! Do We Know</u> where microscopic photographs of drops of water are shown. From one container of plain water, a scientist poured water into several glass containers. On each container he wrote a particular word or phrase. The drop from the bottle labeled "Love" looked like a beautiful snowflake. The drop from the bottle labeled "Hate" looked like it had been taken from a sewer.

If we have the ability to change or charge water, and our bodies are over 90% water, think of the possibilities. What if we took the possibility a step further and turned a glass bottle into a pitcher of water? We might affix a label to the outside affirming what we want in out life — joy, health, love, abundance! What would happen if we drank from this pitcher of water everyday?

A suggestion: Say, "Cancel, cancel, cancel!" after saying or thinking negative thoughts. Meditate twenty minutes a day and breathe away negative emotions or thoughts. Breathe in Light from above into the top of the head and through the body. Breathe red energy of Christ Consciousness into the soles of the feet and through the body. See negativity leaving. Allow pain, disease, worries, fears, sorrows, anger, etc. to find its own way out. We are fortunate to be living in this age. Anger management, Yoga or Reiki classes did not exist in the 15th century!

Henry VII's long-term hatred for the Yorks drew the Duke of Clarence into his family. George's deep desire to be king and his innate despising for the Lancastrians drew him to Henry VII. Part of God's Plan is that we come to the greater realization that while we are each unique individuals, we are also a part of the greater whole. Thus, we return to walk in another's footsteps so that we might learn compassion.

What is the evidence that Edward IV was a bastard? Interestingly enough, there are Edward's mother's statements to that effect. While Henry VII sent his men out to collect and destroy any evidence of the Duchess of York making these declarations, they didn't get all of the records!

What evidence is there that Edward IV's sons, Prince Edward and Prince Richard, were bastards? First, the evidence shows that Edward was already married when he married Elizabeth Woodville! Second, Edward came down with a severe case of the measles when he was nineteen years old. There is a good probability that it left him sterile. Third, there is the matter of Queen Elizabeth's vanity! Would she sit by while Edward had affair after affair and not have intimate liaisons of her own? She had other children by her first marriage! Did she realize after two years of marriage that Edward was unable to make her pregnant?

Why don't I believe that Richard III was planning on marrying his niece, Princess Elizabeth? A marriage between two blood relatives that close would have been deemed exceedingly inappropriate at best. Even under the most pressing of situations, Richard, who was devoutly religious, never would have gotten papal approval for the union! He never would have asked!

Why did I use horsemanship as one of the ways to reveal Richard's personality? It is something that I know and it is generally accepted that authors write best about subjects that they are familiar with. In addition, the skills of good horsemanship personify the Duke of York's personal and professional beliefs; the convictions that he would have impressed upon his sons through word and example.

Where did the description of the Master of the Henchmen come from? Some images come clearer than others. The Master of the Henchmen is an image with lucidity. If this man was not the Master of the Henchmen, he was certainly someone who powerfully influenced Richard III.

Why do I believe that Richard III had a mystical experience? Individuals, who have such experiences, have a rare glimpse of the wonders that lay beyond physical reality. While they may still be concerned with advancement, their motives involve higher incentives. Such individuals cease to be an entity apart, solely preoccupied with materialism. They look to the common good and the welfare of those around them. Fear of death diminishes! Does this describe Richard III?

What about the story that another body had been substituted for Henry IV? In <u>Cruel Kings and Mean Queens</u> by Terry Deary, he gives the following evidence on page 102. This supports the contention that superstitious sailors threw Henry IV's body, which they believed was hexed, overboard in a storm:

> "A silly story, but . . . the king's tomb was opened in 1832. The archaeologists found . . .
> · The inner coffin was a completely different shape from the outer one — had the swapped body come in its own coffin?
> · The space between them was filled with straw — was this to stop the old coffin rattling and giving the game away?

· *There were no royal riches buried with the body — had the sailors taken the chance to pinch them?*
· *On the inner coffin was a simple cross made of twigs bound together — was that the best the coffin robbers could do for the dead king's soul?"*

Why do I believe that Henry IV had Richard II murdered? At the time, different rumors persisted as to how Richard II died. After Richard II's death, Henry IV suffered from acute guilt and depression, which resulted in chronic illness, massive lice infestation and premature aging. Perhaps, Henry could justify taking Richard's crown without first negotiating for reforms. However, it would be difficult for Henry IV to rationalize Richard II's cold-blooded murder under the circumstances. Henry IV's symptoms belong in the category of a murderer, not an overly ambitious man!

While I am working on a book, information sometimes comes in a sudden surprise of inner knowing. One of these realizations was that Henry V came back as Louis XI. Only the Great Screenwriter is capable of creating high drama on this scale! Louis XI in France undid what Edward III and Henry V set up! It may be argued that some wars are justifiable. However, it is also true that through military incarnations a soul sees the futility of conquest, and of imposing a way of life or religion on another group of people. On his deathbed Napoleon longed for one last battle. He returned as a combatant serving in the front line of World War I. In addition, those who advocate war but send others into battle most certainly return in another lifetime or lifetimes as foot soldiers.

Follow Up

My childhood growing up as a devout Catholic, who had beyond the ordinary experiences, is touched upon in <u>Reiki & Other Rays of Touch Healing</u> as well as in <u>Between Two Worlds: The Story of Henry VIII and Anne Boleyn — and Her Celtic Heritage</u>. Within <u>Between Two Worlds</u> I also go into the metaphysical factors and experiences that helped develop my creative writing skills. Some readers of <u>Between Two Worlds</u> have commented that they find these and other psychic experiences intriguing; however, they would be frightened at the prospect of having such experiences themselves. These individuals may be interested in the 5th edition of <u>Reiki & Other Rays of Touch Healing</u> or the 3rd edition of <u>Tera, My Journey Home: Alternative Healing</u> in which extraordinary phenomenon is explained in ordinary language. These books also go into how to safely open and develop psychic abilities. There are also techniques for clearings and soul rescue. I believe that extraordinary abilities are tools that we might all have at our disposal, but the most important thing we do while in body is to pay attention and live in the moment.

Rather than rehash the same material that is included my other books, it serves the purpose of this book to continue on, clarifying where necessary. In the back of this book I have included some reviews of my books and videos. Just to give an idea of where I am coming from, the following is a review written by Susan Dobra of <u>Between Two Worlds</u>, which appeared in the spring 2004 issue of <u>Magical Blend Magazine</u>:

"Whenever a story is set in a distant time and place and dramatized, as this one is, we *usually call it historical fiction. But Kathleen Ann Milner's story of Henry VIII and Anne Boleyn has an interesting claim on historical accuracy. Milner believes she was Boleyn in a past life. She details the evidence for her belief in the second half of this fascinating book, and makes a convincing enough case that the story presented in the first half appears in a whole new light."*

"We all know the story of King Henry's penchant for lopping off the heads of his wives — Anne Boleyn was the second of his six. She is often treated unkindly by historians as a usurper to the queen's throne. Milner sees it differently. She presents Boleyn as a sympathetic figure, and also weaves in the details of her skills in Celtic magic, taught to her by her grandmother. Between Two Worlds is a spellbinding book that brings to life Anne Boleyn's precarious place in one of the most treacherous social structures ever to exist. It deftly humanizes the key players and artfully engages the reader with its surprising revelations. If you're interested in what it was really like in the court of Henry VIII, you should read Between Two Worlds. This could be the true story."

When one aspect of a life improves, other pieces of character and seemingly unrelated abilities are mysteriously enhanced as well. In my particular life, when my riding or how I am able to handle horses improves, my writing improves as well. A logical explanation may be that good horseback riding involves sophisticated right/left brain coordination. So does good writing, painting, etc.!

The left logical brain learns the techniques and information necessary to operate and deal with a variety of important tasks in the physical world. Left-brain learning involves memorization, task completion, formulation, discernment, categorization, and the wisdom necessary to function judiciously. The right creative brain receives imaginative and innovative ideas from the World of Spirit or the Otherworld. Right-brain learning is enhanced through meditation. The idea is to surprise the left brain with truths that the right brain is able to discern from the Otherworlds. In this way, the left brain begins to allow the right brain to function. For example, when information or healings from Shamanic Journeys are confirmed, the logical left brain has to begin to accept ingenious, imaginative thoughts from the right brain. The left brain may then act upon artistic thoughts from the right brain.

In the creative process the idea is to eventually coordinate the thinking of both brains so that both brains are functioning at the same time. It is possible to think creatively and logically at the same time! Like a pianist, in horseback riding one leg may be doing one thing, the other leg another thing, and each one of the arms something else. Each part of the body operates independently to perform the skills necessary to signal the horse. At the same time, the rider tunes in to feel the horse's energy. She or he visualizes the next movement, like a musician, who while playing one measure is looking ahead at the next.

Four of the horses who found their way into my life had been abused. Two of those were severely battered, horribly neglected. Their stories were told in previous books. Abez and Sam's tales are in the chapter, *Animals and Healing,* in Reiki & Other Rays of Touch Healing; Buckley (a.k.a. Bucky), Christie, Duchess and Melchizedek are in the chapter, *Storm's Fury's Last Son,* in Tera, My Journey Home: Alternative Healing, 3rd Edition. Their stories are continued within the second half of Between Two Worlds.

In *Tera, My Journey Home,* the chapter, *Storm's Fury's Last Son,* ended with the statement that my Saddlebred was ridable and that he was going to be all right. Bucky had come a long way! He was present in his body and had stopped zoning out. He allowed me on his back without incident. Because he had lost a lot of his fear, he was more confident. He loved and he knew he was loved. However, Bucky had issues to work out. He was still learning how to be a horse again. Sometimes Bucky ran through the bridle; he needed to carry himself more. He also needed to have respect without fear of terrible reprisals. He was ridable at the walk and trot!

Saddlebreds are bred to trot! If an individual is looking for a Saddlebred to work with, purchase or breed, he will go out into the pasture, create a loud, sudden ruckus and watch to see which horse trots straight out rather than canter or gallop off. He is looking for the one that trots straight out.

The confirmation that makes a Saddlebred an extremely good trotter (collected or extended) also makes it difficult for the Saddlebred to canter. In order to canter with a rider on his back, a Saddlebred has to lift his back up, which is a collection that is difficult for any horse to do. At prestigious Saddlebred shows you will see riders running horses into the wall with the neck of his horse curved towards the wall in an attempt to get a canter from their horse.

Because Saddlebreds are typically long, the other movement that is difficult for them to do is bend their ribcage around the inside leg of the rider. When a horse travels in a circle (not a square), his whole body should demonstrate the identical arch of the circle. Circles are difficult because the inside hind leg has to come up and under; thus, it makes a shorter step. The movement a horse makes while executing a circle is a form of collection. Under the circumstances, the task of completing Bucky's training was better left in someone else's hands.

In December 2003, Bucky fell out of his stall. I had a farrier, Tommy Coley, apply pressure along the leg to see what kind of reaction he was able to get. It was the suspensory ligament! Typically, an injury of this nature takes six months to heal and a full year before the horse is completely sound.

I did hands-on healing in Bucky's aura, on the touchpoint for connective tissue and on the leg itself. Afterwards, I put mud with herbs and essential oils on both front legs. As Bucky is a hot horse, I opted to leave the backdoor to his stall open, so he could walk around the adjoining paddock, which was packed with shavings. The next day, I had Tommy palpate the leg again. It was better! Because Bucky continued to improve, I did not change what I was doing.

In the last week of January, Tommy was unable to get a reaction. As Bucky had been bounding about in the paddock, Tommy felt that I could begin hand walking him. Just on an impulse, I asked Tommy to check Bucky's right leg. Bucky was lame on it; he had compensated with his right leg and it was sore. I worked on both legs!

By the middle of February, I was walking Bucky in hand. Clell Usher, the chiropractor, adjusted Bucky's neck. Apparently, the second/third cervical vertebrae are prone to go out of adjustment when there is a suspensory ligament injury in a front leg. I wanted to go slowly with Bucky, but I kept getting the message that I was holding him back. By the beginning of March, I was on Bucky.

In March, I found a horse trainer to work with Bucky. I had heard about Jim Wenger from Salie Christopher, who was selling Cactus Flower Remedies at a metaphysical fair. It took place at A Peace of Universe where I was signing my books. Salie works intuitively — her clients ask her,

"What remedy is best for me at this time?" Salie goes into a meditative state and asks her angles. After considering the person and situation, she intuitively goes through the bottles, selecting what is required. It is then up to her client to decide which, if any, of the remedies to purchase.

The Cactus Flower Remedy she selected for me was Saguaro-Queen Formula, which is for people who need to balance their masculine and feminine natures. It didn't seem fit! Rather than just dismissing her, I tuned into my own angels to ask, "Why did Salie choose this for me?" When the answer came, I asked Salie, "Is this for my horse, Bucky?"

Sali tuned in, surprised to find out that I was right. Then another light bulb went off. I asked her, "Is this for Christie as well?"

Again Salie tuned in; again she received an affirmative. It made perfect sense. Bucky was macho-macho-man. Christie was like the delicate princess, who in the fairy tale was able to detect a pea under a pile of one hundred mattresses. Then Salie added, "My best friend's husband is a horse trainer. Jim works intuitively. He would do a good job with your horse."

I didn't call Jim Wenger immediately. When I called Salie to tell her that the Cactus Flower Remedy, Akashic Records, she had recommended for me worked, she said, "I went out to dinner with Jim and Diane Wenger last night. Jim said that if he were you, he would change Bucky's name."

The problem was that Bucky's name had been changed several times and for good reasons. The horse did need to lose the rodeo name! He also needed consistency! Bucky's registered name is Storm's Fury's Big Bucks, with Stormy or Fury arguably being more violently than Bucky. I tried a derivative of Bucky. When I called, "Buckley!" he responded.

However, he cocked his head ever so slightly at the addition of the letter 'L', as if to say, "Did I hear this right?" There is a lot in a name! With a gentleman's name, Buckley made a shift for the better. Saguaro-Queen also helped!

I called Jim Wenger, fully explaining Buckley's situation. Buckley had been abused, rehabilitated, stolen, re-abused, grossly neglected, recovered through court action, and was in the process of being re-rehabilitated. Jim came out to Santa Rita to meet Buckley! Jim trains three-year-old horses to go under saddle; he also works with ridable horses that have problems. After watching me ride, Jim got on board. He was firm without being harsh. His training and riding methods were unique, ranging between Western and dressage with his own intuitive methods added into the formula. However, Jim's idea of collection was different from rigid German dressage techniques. In the spring of 2004, Buckley was put into training with Jim.

Riding instructors in the past have told me to stop putting my weight on the stirrups and keep my weight in my ankles. Jim demonstrated that if a rider's weight is in the ankles then the ankles have lost their flexibility; the ankles are no longer shock absorbers! The rider balances on the stirrups by standing on them with the balls of the feet. The heels are down and the legs rest flexibility against the horse's sides. If not, the rider either balance on the reins, or grips with the knees, or legs. Gripping is contradictory to the final objective, whereby the horse is soft in the mouth and responsive to the slightest pressure of the calves, knees and seat. How is a horse able to respond to slight leg pressure changes when the rider is always gripping him?

Riders with so-called 'hot seats' are often clutching their horses and making them go. They may or may not know they are doing this. Hot-seat riders often have to ride with spurs because their horses are dead to the leg. If there is always constant pressure from the legs, horses are unable to ascertain a difference between a constant clutch and an additional squeeze. It's not the horse's fault! It is much easier for the horse to detect differences if the leg is steady against his sides. Then a squeeze, or a bump from the calves, or active legs that move alternately in a marching-like manner are different from the steady leg. It is not gripping with the legs that gives a rider a steady leg; rather, it is keeping the weight in the balls of the feet and the seat bones on the saddle that produces a firm leg.

I told the story in <u>Tera, My Journey Home</u> of how I was on Buckley when he took off mindlessly, bucking, galloping, hopping and pitching in the air. (Typically, when a horse starts bucking, the rider puts his/her leg on the horse to get the horse to move forward so that the horse stops.) Then Buckley headed towards the hot walker; my head was the same height as the arms of the hot walker. At that point, I was forced to dismount, exiting from his right side. I landed on my feet, but on the side of my left foot. As the human leg does not bend to the side, my ankle broke.

There was no fear while this was going on. Like other people who are put suddenly into harm's way, I simply reacted as best I could. However, the trauma remained in my body. Jim showed me that my body was reacting to the unreleased stress by gripping Buckley. I wasn't even aware that I was doing it. Buckley and I were both in training with Jim!

Jim schooled Buckley for about a month and then I started riding Buckley again. It took a while to learn to have confidence in Buckley again. As I went through a healing process and relearned how to ride Buckley, my legs relaxed.

As the months continued, I felt as though I was in a University curriculum on horsemanship. What is different about Jim from many, but not all trainers, is that he helps his clients to ride their horses in the same way he is able to ride them. If the horse and rider are being trained properly, there is a love between the horse and owner, and the rider makes an attempt to do what the instructor asks, then the owner of the horse should be the one who is able to get the best response from his or her horse.

Natural balance is a shoeing technique whereby the horse's shoes are set back slightly. A farrier noticed that the hoof tips of wild mustangs were worn. However, he made his observation in the spring after the mustangs foraged for food all winter. While there may be some horses who benefit from natural balance shoeing, my horses moved much better when their shoes were put on in the standardized manner.

Concentrating outside of our sense of self opens the way for ideas or understanding to come in. It became clear that what I was doing with Buckley and Christie was preparing me to ride my two-year-old, Melchizedek, when he was old enough to ride. (A two-year-old horse is not physically, mentally or emotionally prepared for a rider.)
What also came to me quite clearly was that Buckley is a reincarnation of Sam, whom I wrote about in Reiki & Other Rays of Touch Healing. Abez had just died when Sam came into my life. I was not ready to purchase another horse at the time. In looking back, there is nothing that I could have done differently. Life is interesting, when something does not work out at one time, it will later on or in another lifetime.

In the fall of 2003, I was in London, staying at the home of Peter and Brenda Davies.

Brenda was busy proofreading Between Two Worlds when she paused to make a casual statement. "You will be taking small segments of Between Two Worlds and writing other books."

I had just started doing research on a novel about Rembrandt, his art and his illegitimate daughter. (She was kept a well kept secret. Many people in the Netherlands are unaware that Rembrandt had a daughter. However, there is proof of her existence.) After Brenda's statement, I was very much aware of the presence of the spirit of Richard III. Of course, it was my choice, but he really wanted his story told.

When I started writing, the strongest impressions that came in from the spirit of Richard III were emotionally charged events from that lifetime, not necessarily in chronological order. Thus, I found myself skipping ahead and going backwards into the story even more than usual. One day, the impression came to write about George's death. It was not a thrilling prospect, elaborating on how the Yeomen held George's head in a barrel of wine while his arms and legs flailed about! Setting my preconceptions aside, a subtle thought, quieter than a whisper, came into the middle of my brain. Begin the day before George's execution.

As I wrote, events played themselves out in a surprising way. I shared the story that is in the chapter, *The Man Who Would Be King,* with several people. Those who were psychic had chills of confirmation or received their own verification. Most said, "Of course! This makes perfect sense!"

Another example of being open, rather than trying to force writing, is the storyline of the Stone of Scone. I knew within the core of my being that the monks of Scone Abbey had switched stones on Edward I, sending the real one off in a small cart to Ireland. I could see it in my mind's eye! In that same moment of revelation, I also knew that the monks had put some kind of enchantment on the stone. However, I was unable to get the details. Rather than worrying about leaving a loose end or making something up, I began the story of the Stone in the first chapter. After writing 170 pages, the answer came. I knew what the monks had done. The story in *Power Without Love* also rings true.

Because the story given to me by the spirit, who presents himself as Richard III, is simple and logical, I believe him to be Richard III. The truth is always straightforward; lies are convoluted! Have I seen this spirit with my physical eyes? I don't often see the Otherworlds with my physical eyes, and have never seen Richard in this way. Visual impressions come into my inner eye. The text itself seems to drip like warm honey into the center of my brain.

Sometimes, a different soul from the 15th century presented him/herself. It helped to get a better sense of his or her character. As I came to the end of this book, I realized that as I wrote, many of these souls went through a healing.

Where does healing come from? All healing comes from God! Nowhere in any edition of any Bible is a devil given credit for healing anyone. Jesus and men and women who were called saints healed. The Order of Melchizedek is a priesthood of healers mentioned in both the New and Old Testaments. I am simply a channel for this energy!

One day, I was impressed to stop writing altogether and send healing. Where? To clear the magic that was put on the imitation Stone of Scone. In my mind's eye I could see the brownish-gray figures of the monks who had called the curse into the stone. In life they were surprised at the energy they created; in death they were reluctantly obliged to remain behind in order to fulfill the foreshadowing. In like manner, Babe Ruth was obliged to fulfill the curse he put on the Boston Red Socks. In September 2004, there was a shift, as if the Bambino was ready to move on. When he let go, the Red Socks were able to win.

If the mind is quiet and the spirit is open events in everyday life have the potential of becoming life-altering ideas. An off-handed remark from a friend, acquaintance or stranger may change our perceptions. Ideas may also come from a movie.

We create in the quantum physics field of possibilities through our concentrated attention. This may be done through meditation or Shamanic Journeys or focusing outside of us. The movie, What the #$*! Do We Know, takes the process one step further. That is, we are also able to ask God for a confirmation. To paraphrase one of the scientists in the movie: "I have created my day. God, give me a sign so that I know You are listening. Let this sign come in a surprising and unexpected way so that I know it comes from You."

How many of us are told that The Almighty expects us to ask questions? Rather than make inquires, we plead for this and that, without asking God what He has in mind. Nor are we told that if we ask, the answer will come! The result of not asking and not listening is that we engage in a limited, one-sided dialog, whereby we are doing all the talking with The Creator of All There Is. Without communication we set perimeters, narrowly defining who we are. At the same time, we create God in our image and judge Him in terms of His ability to listen to us. Our perceptions are clouded with thoughts that if our prayers are answered, it is a miracle; if not, we have done something wrong.

If we ask God we will receive an answer! When that answer comes as clear as a bell, we are able to proceed optimistically on that course without reservation. We are able to walk through fear, doubts and worry to the other side, wondering what is waiting for us. Oftentimes, God's plan for us appears illogical or there is a risk involved. By trusting in the answer we

258

receive and holding true to that answer, we are able to see the course through to the end. No risk, no gain! Big risk, big gain! Richard III and his contemporaries did not have the advantage of this wisdom!

One of the other insights that came to me while writing this book was how to help people release creative blockages. Then afterwards open the right brain to receive insights from and work with angels and spirit guides in the creative process. As an experiment, fifteen people took a Thursday off from work after a book talk/signing in Limerick. The healing energy I channel enabled workshop participants to release blockages. Because I am connected to creativity and am able to tune into the Otherworlds, I was able to help others do likewise. Everyone involved felt that the experiences through the day resulted in a significant breakthrough.

How do I know about what happens to a soul after death? I saw Abez's spirit running free in a beautiful place in nature after he died. It is one of the reasons why earthbound souls, who come to me for help, trust that they are going to a better place.

There have been individuals who have laughed at my healing abilities, even though they have seen miracles. I am not sure why they continue to disbelieve that God works through all of us in seemingly unexpected and surprising ways? One such individual was Mallory Davies, a beautiful, blond teenager. It never bothered me that Mallory or some of the other boarders at Santa Rita found me weird. They had a right to their opinion.

Mallory died when her vehicle was forced off the road. She was thrown from the truck, breaking her neck upon impact. I had a suspicion that she had not gone on when different people at the stable remarked that they had experienced her presence in different ways. It was on the day of her funeral, when I realized that she was asking me for help through these individuals. She was stuck between the worlds! Grief from her many friends and family held her back, as did the fact that she did not understand the dying process. I asked the angels to open the vortex. Afterwards, I asked Mallory to take the hand of an angel and go into the Light. As she began her ascent, I chanted an affirmation to assist her on her journey. She may have laughed at me when she was alive, but she felt she could trust me in death!

Grief is not the only thing that holds souls back. In the spring of 2004, my brother, Tom, died. He had suffered from a severe chemical imbalance since he was eighteen years old. A Beautiful Mind told the story of how one man was able to overcome his severe illness. Tom's case was worse! My mother derived comfort when I suggested to her that Tom was working out karma from another lifetime and that his next life would be better.

Tom died from a toxic combination of chemotherapy and the medicine for his mental disorder. In life, when he was lucid, he was a devout Catholic; in death, he was confused. I asked Tracy Lawler Boen, to work with me to help Tom. While Tracy watched Tom in her mind's eye, I created more healing energy through my breath and with symbols. At last, a woman whom Tom had known came to him. Tracy was not able to hear what she said. When Tom took a hold of her hand, she did not let go. Together, they walked into the vortex of Light, which has been described by many individuals, who have had near-death experiences, as a beautiful tunnel through which they travel upwards to a loving presence.

People who commit suicide do not escape their problems! In addition, they find themselves trapped between the worlds. One of my therapist's daughters shot herself in the head with a rifle. Afterwards, his youngest daughter was able to see the spirit of her dead sister. Other members of the family were able to perceive her presence.

Oftentimes, when one sibling commits suicide, there is a danger that other siblings may do the same. This is because the spirit of the one who committed suicide is haunting the home. It is not that that spirit wishes to inflict harm; rather, that spirit still holds the negative emotional state and mental thoughts that brought him or her to commit suicide in the first place. The other children may believe that these strong thoughts are their own.

My therapist was able to feel his daughter in front of him. It seemed that she was trying to feel the love that had been offered to her throughout her life. She was doing this for the benefit of her sisters. While he focused on his daughter, I worked with the angels. It took an effort, but she did go to the Light!

The souls of those knights who participated in the not-so Holy Crusades were often included in the clearings at Canterbury and elsewhere. The knights' motives had been the highest. Rome had provided a horrific depiction of Moslems, which in reality was a grossly distorted lie. The Pope guaranteed deliverance from sin and heavenly rewards beyond description to the crusaders. The real motive, the power that would come to the Church by controlling the Holy Land, was kept from the knights. The so-called holy war was entirely about supremacy and wealth. (A case could be made that every major war has been about controlling this rather large piece of real estate. Even World War II!)

There is an old saying, "The road to hell is paved with good intentions." It's also said that more harm has been done in the name of God or Christ than anyone else, even Hitler or Napoleon. The crusades were no exception. Knights inflicted mayhem and horrendously slaughtered countless people. In one conflict, knights stood ankle-deep in Moslem blood. The knights, those who sent them and those who supported them were held accountable through the Laws of Karma. Many, if not all, of these personalities reincarnated in the Middle East. If karma is not completely worked out, this personality of the greater soul remains stuck between the worlds. Soul rescue is possible through Universal healing energy.

Some people point to the fact that because I talk about my own shortcomings and injuries, it is an indication that I am lacking, and that the healing system, Tera-Mai™, is faulty. Demigods and pedestals do not hold much appeal! It has been my hope that in talking about healing my own issues that it has helped others to heal.

What else did I do besides hands-on healing? The left ankle, which broke after dismounting Buckley while he was galloping and bucking towards the hot walker, now looks very much like the right. There is no calcium ring or even a line on either the tibia or fibula, both of which were broken cleanly through. When the cast came off, I went to Ed Sheridan, a myopractitioner for therapy. Myopractic therapy works on specific points along tendons and muscles to help them release. It is quite painful, but the relief afterwards is worthwhile. I now have the same extension and flexion in both ankles.

W-Zymes by Michael's Naturopathic Programs are very much like Wobenzymes but less expensive and the dosage is less. Proteolytic enzymes aid digestion if several are taken one half hour before meals. One clever individual figured out that if enough enzymes were taken on an empty stomach, the enzymes work to heal and even rebuild cartilage and connective tissue. I take either fifteen Wobenzymes or eleven W-Zymes with water first thing in the morning. Then I wait for an hour and a half to two hours before eating or drinking anything else except more water. Enzymes may be taken on an empty stomach in the evening before going to bed (at least four hours after eating). Those who wake up in the middle of the night may take enzymes with water then.

Besides the information in the chapter, *Herbs, supplements and Iridology,* in the 3rd edition of <u>Tera, My Journey Home</u> I have found that CetylPure by Natrol nourishes connective tissue. Internally, Mangosteen helps heal connective tissue; externally, Emu oil absorbs quickly and heals wounds. Rubbing swollen bones and cartilage for ten minutes a day helps the swelling to go down. Sore No-More by Equilite is a horse product that works particularly well on my muscles.

A secondary function of connective tissue is to absorb toxins that the liver and kidneys are unable to take care of. I mentioned in <u>Tera, My Journey Home</u> that this may be a reason why some people's noses, ears and joints get bigger with age. The difficulty is in releasing these toxins.

Fat and water-soluble toxins need a carrier in order to leave the body. Water pressure in colonics pulls toxins from all over the body. Taking a product, such as, Livatone the night before a colon therapy session helps toxins to exit the body. If the walls of the intestines are cleaned through a series of colonics, toxins are better able to dump into the large colon so that they may be flushed out. When the intestinal walls are clean, one may want to do a lymphatic massage or other forms of aggressive detoxing. Then follow up with a colonic so that the toxins that have been stirred up may be released. For those who do not believe in colonics, just look at Goldie Hawn and Bette Midler.

For a long time, the surface muscles in my neck were so tight that the therapists were unable to get to a deep muscle, which tore and healed with scaring. (I was rear ended on December 6, 2000.) Finally, when the outer muscles relaxed, the therapists were able to get to the scar tissue to start working it out. The supplements mentioned previously also helped. In addition, I used magnate therapy (only the north end of the magnate touches the body). Like other healers, I can work on myself but I am more effective when I work on other people.

In my particular case, it was important for me to not pursue the under and uninsured motorist coverage I had under my automobile insurance company. Edward IV understood how important it is to pick battles! Personally, dealing with corrupt and inept attorneys, lies from the woman who hit me, and a greedy insurance company had taken a lot of energy just to get some money out of the insurance company of the woman who hit me. It wasn't even enough to cover all of the medical bills! When I received the impression to let the matter go, I did! While it was illogical, I did it! As a result, not only was I able to write this book in 3 1/2 months, but there was also a window of opportunity for me to heal.

Rosemarie Siciliano, my colon therapist, purchased a Platinum Energy System, which is based on an Ancient Chinese remedy. The healee puts his or her feet into a small tub of salt water, which is energized to attract positive and negative ions. The water in the foot spa becomes an extension of the water in the body, separated by a thin membrane of skin. During the half hour session, most people will turn the water a dark brown color; heavy metals coalesce into small, black spots or balls, and scum from the liver or gall bladder may also form on the top of the water. By having a colon therapy session afterwards, I personally felt that additional toxins are released. www.platinumenergysystems.com

The machine also pulls toxicity from areas in the body where there has been surgery. The first time Rosemarie used the machine, she felt a release in her left ankle, which she broke about the same time that I broke mine. Where I noticed it in my body was a bit of a relaxation in my neck. It is interesting; whenever we let go on one level, other levels follow. Little alterations in our daily lives may change the way we think or feel. This may bring modifications or transformations. If we change the way we think, we change our whole lives!

In looking through the story of Richard III, one is able to see clearly that at many different points in his life he could have easily changed the outcome. If Richard had married the Princesses to the lords of the realm, Henry Tudor's cause would have ended. Had Richard been willing to put his prejudice aside and allowed France to arise as a nation-state by signing a treaty with Louis XI, Henry Tudor's cause would have ended. If Richard had spared Hastings and Anthony Woodville and executed Stanley instead, Richard's prospects would have been better.

It is advisable to pout remorsefully about things that could or should have been. It is to suggest that we oftentimes forget to ask God for direction or an affirmation that we are on the right page. Those, like Richard and Anthony Woodville, who did have mystical experiences, did not understand their transcendental nature. They had no idea of how to develop this aspect within themselves or even if they should. Richard and his companions in the fifteenth century did not know they had such options. We do!

Bibliography

Abbott, G., <u>Mysteries of the Tower of London</u>, Hendon Publishing Company, copyright © 1998

Ackroyd, Peter, <u>Albion: The Origins of the English Imagination</u>, Chatto & Windus, copyright © 2002

Ashley, Mike, <u>British Kings & Queens</u>, Barnes & Noble Inc., copyright © 1998

Astill, Grenville and Grant, Annie, <u>The Countryside of Medieval England</u>, Blackwell Publishers, Oxford, copyright © 1988

Barber, Richard, <u>Myths and Legends of the British Isles</u>, Barnes and Noble, Inc., copyright © 2000

Black, Maggie, <u>The Medieval Cookbook</u>, British Museum Press, copyright © 1992

Cheetham, Anthony, <u>The Life and Times of Richard III</u>, George Weidenfeld and Nicolson Limited and Book Club Associates © 1972

Cunningham, Sean, <u>Richard III a Royal Enigma</u>, The National Archives, Kew, Richmond, Surrey, Great Britain, copyright © 2003

Deary, Terry, <u>Horrible Histories, Cruel Kings and Mean Queens</u>, Commonwealth House, copyright © 1995

Deary, Terry, <u>Horrible Histories, The Measley Middle Ages</u>, Commonwealth House, copyright © 1996

De Rosa, Peter, <u>Vicars of Christ: The Dark Side of the Papacy</u>, Bantam Press, Great Britain, copyright © 1988

Dockray, Keith, <u>Richard III A Source Book</u>, Sutton Publishing Limited, Thrupp, Stroud, Gloucestershire, Great Britain, copyright © 1997

Fraser, Antonia, <u>The Lives of the Kings & Queens of England</u>, George Weidenfeld and Nicholson, Ltd., paperback edition published by The Orion Publishing Company, copyright © 1975, 1993, 1998

Hartley, Dorothy, <u>Lost Country Life</u>, Pantheon Books, New York, © 1979

Head, Joseph & Cranston, S.L., <u>Reincarnation: The Phoenix Fire Mystery</u>, Julian Press/Crown Publishers, Inc., New York, copyright © 1977

Hopkins, Andrea, <u>A Chronicle History of Knights</u>, Barnes & Noble Books, Copyright © 2004

Jenner, Michael, <u>Journeys into Medieval England</u>, Penguin Group, London, copyright © 1991

Kendall, Paul Murray, <u>Richard III</u>, W. W. Norton & Company, New York & London, copyright © 1955, 1956, 1983, 1984

Plowden, Alison, <u>Tudor Women: Queens & Commoners</u>, George Weidenfeld and Nicholson, Ltd., revised edition by Sutton Publishing Limited, Gloucestershire, Great Britain, copyright © 1979, 1998

Pollard, A. J., Richard III and the Princes in the Tower, Sutton Publishing Limited — Phoenix Mill, Thropp, Scroud, Gloucestershire, copyright © 1991

Ridley, Jasper, Henry VIII, Guild Publishing, London, second edition published 1985 by Book Club Associates, copyright © 1984

Robinson, John Martin, Royal Residences, Macdonald & Co., London & Sydney, copyright © 1982

Stevens, Serita Deborah with Klarner, Anne, Deadly Doses, a Writer's Guide to Poisons, Writer's Digest Books, Cincinnati, Ohio, copyright © 1990

Further research provided from visits to sites, museums and art galleries in Great Britain, and brochures without author or copyright. A special thank you to English Heritage, and the knowledgeable guides of the Open Book Visitor Guiding.

Tera-Mai™

Willem Boern has been involved in a 4-year Spirituality Course in The Netherlands. As part of the work he was doing, in the summer of 2004, Willem asked if he could read my aura. The process took over an hour.

When Willem got to my crown (the top of my head), he saw Tera-Mai™ below me, Buddha above me and a giant star above Buddha representing God. I was between Buddha and Tera-Mai™ nailed to a cross. Willem was able to get the nails out, but he was unable to get me off the cross. I was left tied to the cross between Buddha and Tera-Mai™.

What does this mean? Almost 30 years ago, I asked God if He would reconnect me to the psychic and healing abilities I had as a young girl. Meeting Buddha in a consciousness-raising experience, whereby my physical, mental, emotional and spiritual bodies were in the Otherworlds was not the end of the process. Since I first prayed to God, He has continued to increase my healing and psychic abilities. However, since my encounter with Buddha, I have been pulling up Tera-Mai™ behind me in my effort to fully engage the promise of psychic and healing abilities in my astrological natal birth chart. The imagery of me on a cross represents what I have sacrificed and endured for the healing system, Tera-Mai™.

When I asked God to show me what I had given up for Tera-Mai™, I was shown a huge, purple mountain. I fully understand that there are not many people who would be willing to give up so much for a healing system. I also understand that the contract people, who want to be able to administer the higher initiations in Tera-Mai™ are asked to sign, is not for everyone. Only those individuals, who have absolutely no questions in their minds about being dedicated to Tera-Mai™ and are willing to abide by the terms of the contract, should consider signing it.

Willem also got strongly that Tera-Mai™ has never, ever happened before! There has never, ever been a school without walls for higher initiations. In past societies, higher initiations were only given within the temple. As secrecy and integrity are still important aspects in a school without walls, a strongly binding contract is mandatory in this physical world. In light of what I have undergone, this is a small request.

Understanding what I have gone through to bring Tera-Mai™ into being as a recognized healing system throughout the world, one might have a better comprehension of why simply receiving Tera-Mai™ initiations and trying to use the energy for manmade attunements is inappropriate at best. Is it any wonder why manmade attunements fail to survive the test of time? They never have!

On the same trip to Europe, I was shown how to fully clear Tera-Mai™ and myself everyday. Everyday I ask God to send more abilities and powers of healing, divination and manifestation to Buddha and into myself. From myself, I ask that these energies be past into Tera-Mai™ to only the properly attuned Tera-Mai™ initiates, who are free from black magic and free from manmade attunements. In addition, I ask that everyone and anyone else be removed from Tera-Mai™ and myself.

Since understanding how to pray and visualize in order to achieve my goal, I have been rising up closer to Buddha. My own healing and psychic abilities have increased spectacularly. I would be a mad woman were in not for the fact that the healing and psychic abilities of those Tera-Mai™ initiates, who are free from black magic and free from manmade attunements, is also increasing dramatically. As this book goes to the printers in November 2004, I feel that by Christmas my prayer will have answered and I will free of the cross. As one door close and another opens.

Video & Audiotape Mail Order

Kathleen Milner, PMB 281, 9393 N. 90th St.,
Scottsdale, AZ 85258
www.kathleenmilner.com

Check or money order includes handling and ground postage

Videos $35 each
Healing Hands subtitled Reiki I
Symbols in Healing subtitled Reiki II
Healing Animals

Audiotapes $11 each
Candle Meditation: Meditator guided into the "gap" between thought and breath through spiritual techniques taught in ancient mystery schools. Some meditators are able to hear and experience the qualities of Angeliclight. Crystal Cave on side 2 begins and ends in a crystal cave. In between, it is a space journey where the mediator discovers healing and self-empowerment.

Journey to Sacred Mountain: Incorporates the 4 directions, 4 elements, and Mother-Father God into our own heart centers, which is where sacred mountain lies. Ancient Symbology on side 2 works with Universal archetypal energies found within Egyptian hieroglyphs. Mediator is guided into the Sphinx and Great Pyramid.

When the Angels Came: Healing journey with angels to the vortexes and power places on Mother Earth. Passageways, music only by Richard Bennett on side 2.

Past Life Regression: Begins with a healing meditation for the physical body and concludes with a healing for the past life that was experienced. <u>Shaman's Journey</u> on side 2 is a meditation whereby the mediator experiences colors with the help of symbols and the Shaman's drum.

Atlantian Heart Chakra Meditation: Group meditation using candles and combined consciousness to explore other realities and to bring back healing for the members of the group and for Mother Earth. From a meditation called Synergy that was channeled to William Buehler, a priest in the Church of Antioch. <u>Atlantis</u>, music only by Paul Lincoln, on side 2.

Other Books by Kathleen Milner

Tera, My Journey Home: Seichem, Shamanism, Symbology, Herbs & Reincarnation ISBN 1-886903-12-3, full-color illustrations by author, 308 pages, 8.5 X 11 inches, $21.95

Reiki & Other Rays of Touch Healing ISBN 1-886903-97-2, 152 pages, 8.5 X 11 inches, manual for healers, $15.95

Between Two Worlds: The Story of Henry VIII and Anne Boleyn — and Her Celtic Heritage ISBN 1-886903-21-2, 306 pages, 6 X 9 inches, $15.95

Prints of Illustrations by Kathleen Milner

<u>Babaji & Eight Ascension Symbols</u> - full-color, 8 1/2 X 11 inch print - $11

<u>La Voix - The Voice</u> - Reproduction of a charcoal drawing of the head of the coming Christ. Individually signed, limited edition of 500, 21 X 30 inches - $150

Reviews

Reiki & Other Rays of Touch Healing:
Reviewed in Nov/Dec 1994 **The Inner Voice** by Nancy
Rajala:

  Cover art is a watercolor painted by the
author. . . . A comprehensive manual on
healing. The author gives concrete examples in
both the use of symbols and a variety of healing
techniques interwoven in her own healing process
(following two automobile accidents) and her
subsequent work on the inner planes with Sai Baba
and other teachers. The book explains techniques
that can be utilized to develop psychic abilities
and how to achieve deeper levels of meditation,
and then ties this in with the healing process and
different mysticisms.

  Kathleen offers her readers a fresh,
meaningful understanding of the history of Reiki
combined with Jesus' teachings and related aspects
of other spiritualisms. There are chapters
dealing with the use of healing energy in
ceremonial work and Feng Shui, the Chinese art of
altering life circumstances by altering one's
environment. There's also a chapter devoted to
healing animals, including a story of how a horse
was healed of blindness in two weeks.

  Kathleen believes that all healing energy
comes from the Creative, Loving Force behind this
universe, and the final chapter explains the
dynamics of initiation into rays of healing. If
you are a healer, or you're involved in a healing
process, it is a source you may find yourself
often referring to."

Reiki & Other Rays of Touch Healing 5th Edition

Are you interested in developing your psychic or healing abilities? Going through a healing process? Do you want to understand the phenomenon of spontaneous healing? How do alterative healing methods and techniques work? If Shamanic Journeys and meditation operate in the field of possibilities described in quantum physics, are there specific procedures that aid or hinder the creative process? If so, this still original book may have the answers you seek.

Milner's writing style over the years has evolved into engaging texts that merit savoring as opposed to a quick read. She has an uncanny ability to perceive psychically, which impacts upon her writing, affording her readers the opportunity to observe in a fresh way. Stories and examples of healings are both touching and meaningful. We look forward to her take on Richard III in her soon to be released novel, *White Boar.*

"She's the real deal!" Michael Harrison *Talkers Magazine*

<u>Tera, My Journey Home</u> 2nd edition
Reviewed in March 2000 issue of **Magical Blend** by Kristian Rice

Kathleen Ann Milner is the author of the only two books that are available on Seichem and the aspects of the four elemental healing rays. In her newest edition (second edition) of *Tera, My Journey Home,* she deals with self-healing as a substitute for conventional medical treatment. Her focus is on symptoms, healing energies and the channeling of healing energy, which facilitates self-healing. She has combined Reiki with Buddhist beliefs to unlock this phenomenon. She educates and shares her insights on how to tune into healing and psychic abilities. Readers will find this gem of a book to be an insightful reference to the healing forces hidden within our universe.

Tera, My Journey Home: Alternative Healing
3rd edition
Summer 2004 issue of **Leading Edge Review**

Is your tongue white? Do you wake up tired? Do you have trouble losing or putting on weight? You will discover that the above symptoms are characteristics of secondary infections, which are unresponsive to antibiotics. Milner maps out the whys, hows and practical application of a variety of alternative therapies designed to restore homeostasis for this and other health issues.

Other chapters include a Shamanic & Divination system that may be used by anyone, retraining and therapeutics for abused horses, elemental healing, moving Qi, and healing past lives. Well-written, documented, witnessed accounts and stories of healings, and thought-out examples bestow credibility and meaning.

". . She educates and shares her insights on how to tune into healing and psychic abilities. Readers will find this gem of a book to be an insightful reference to the healing forces hidden within our universe." *2nd edition reviewed in Volume #68 Magical Blend Magazine*

Between Two Worlds; The Story of Henry VIII and Anne Boleyn — and Her Celtic Heritage
Reviewed in **Magical Blend** by Susan Dobra (issue dated June 2004)

Whenever a story is set in a distant time and place and dramatized, as this one is, we usually call it historical fiction. But Kathleen Ann Milner's story of Henry VIII and Anne Boleyn has an interesting claim on historical accuracy. Milner believes se was Boleyn in a past life. She details the evidence for her belief in the second half of this fascinating book, and makes a convincing enough case that the story presented in the first half appears in a whole new light.

We all know the story of King Henry's penchant for lopping off the heads of his wives — Anne Boleyn was the second of six. She is often treated unkindly by historians as a usurper to the queen's throne. Milner sees it differently. She presents Boleyn as a sympathetic figure, and also weaves in the details of her skills in Celtic magic, taught to her by her grandmother. *Between Two Worlds* is a spellbinding book that brings to life Anne Boleyn's precarious place in one of the most treacherous social structures ever to exist. It deftly humanizes the key players and artfully engages the reader with its surprising revelations. If you're interested in what it was really like in the court of Henry VIII, you should read *Between Two Worlds.*

Symbols in Healing: Reiki II
Reviewed in August 1994 **Body Mind Spirit** magazine by Jane Kuhn:
In this video, Kathleen Milner draws and explains the symbols most people are given in Reiki II initiation and goes beyond to explore additional symbols that work to heal. The first symbols that Satya Sai Baba gave her for the purpose of releasing karma and past life issues is shown. Each symbol presented is for a different purpose and for healing a different part of the body. She encourages us to heal the past and create a beautiful life for ourselves in the present.

Healing Hands: Reiki I
Reviewed in August 1994 **Body Mind Spirit** magazine
by Jane Kuhn:

      Kathleen Milner works from the knowledge that all healing comes from God/Goddess and that we are all capable of channeling, healing and experiencing self-healing. She demonstrates working with touch points on the body to get to the root cause behind pain and disease. Angels and spirit guides are actively engaged in the healing process. She encourages participation of the healees as they share what they are experiencing in their minds and bodies as the healing occurs. Visualization and problem-solving techniques that have been used by great scientists and inventors including Thomas Edison and Albert Einstein are discussed. <u>The video and the healing experience are quite impactful. I experienced them first-hand.</u>